AMERICA'S NATURAL WEALTH

Yosemite National Park

One of the great show windows of conservation

AMERICA'S
NATURAL WEALTH

A Story of the Use and Abuse
of Our Resources

by

RICHARD LIEBER

HARPER & BROTHERS PUBLISHERS

NEW YORK AND LONDON

1942

AMERICA'S NATURAL WEALTH

To the Memory of
JAMES PUTNAM GOODRICH
My Governor

Contents

CONTENTS

5. SCENERY

6. SOWING AND REAPING

Foreword

This book is written by one who had a vision, a clear vision of the truth that man cannot obtain fulfillment of his stature if he is too much separated from nature, the truth that human life is inevitably deprived of the joy and the mental health of right adjustment if it is too much restricted by an environment of its own making. There was clear perception of the fact that, eager for immediate comfort and thoughtless about its future, man tends to be negligent, even destructive, of that natural wealth and beauty which is his great spiritual as well as material inheritance.

He who wrote this book realized the greatness of the need to make men more aware of their indispensable partnership with nature, and less eager to be mere profiteers upon her bounty. To organized effort to attain that end we have given the name Conservation.

To this great mission of Conservation, Richard Lieber has freely given the ripe years of his life. No man has achieved more than he in the magnificent task of saving for his fellow citizens "America as God made her."

He has been no mere theorist, no mere talker about things that should be done. He has done them. He is definitely, and in the best sense of the word, a "practical" man, an achiever of results. His record as Director of Conservation in Indiana, and as organizer of her magnificent system of state parks, is unsurpassed. Not content with that alone, he has

FOREWORD

been for many years a leader in the national planning of parks, and of Conservation.

It is rare indeed to find in one man philosophical depth and profound classical scholarship combined with high executive ability. Dr. Lieber has all of these. The efficiency of his enterprise and management has been no less than the truth and beauty of his vision. In Indiana he has been the chief artisan of a superb creation which will have profound effect upon her citizenry for generations yet to come.

This book should appeal strongly to all who possess enough of constructive imagination to realize the vast import of Conservation. The book portrays its author's vision and defines those steps that must be taken if America's natural heritage, so precious and so irreplaceable, is to be preserved for her people.

The joy of life depends upon attainment of an adjustment to environment that permits fulfillment of the individual's highest possibilities. Richard Lieber has devoted his life to enlargement of opportunity for his fellow citizens to find happiness through enrichment of experience and perception thereby of life's true significance.

STANLEY COULTER

Preface

My aim in this book is to set forth the nature of our material wealth in its bearing upon national security and prosperity, civic and political betterment and finally upon individual happiness, success and spiritual elevation.

The presentation of this situation contains nothing not already known by close students of conservation nor would I be so presumptuous, knowing of the vast scope of their researches, to attempt carrying coals to Newcastle. My intent is rather to attract the interest and to arouse the fighting spirit of intelligent laymen and laywomen on behalf of the great cause of national conservation. This movement today has become one of the most active forces for human betterment.

As a small token of my affection this book is dedicated to the dear memory of one who as Governor of my State instituted a much desired Department of Conservation and furthered its purposes unerringly. His keen intelligence and rare imagination not only made him understand the temper of his constituents but enabled him to translate their hopes and desires into concrete serviceable performance. James P. Goodrich, a singular, but entirely harmonious combination of vision and hardheaded business sense, was approached by those who sensed the common will. To their surprise they found his vision aiming higher even than their own goal and, at times, were somewhat perplexed by observing that his unfailing business sense only furnished the control, but not the motive power, for that free-running engine of social service he set out to operate. Before the Legislature of 1917 went into session he had passed on the draft of a bill for the creation of the Department of Conservation. It failed of passage, was reintroduced in 1919, and became a law.

His actions were a perfect illustration how American leadership operates and in turn set free in others will and capacity for service. All healthy growth must come up from the ground. All lasting gains in our country must be mass gains. Inherent in the people is the strength and the capacity for great accomplishment, but this strength must be liberated and that is the function of a true leader.

I know of no greater endeavor to achieve human happiness, welfare and national security than that of conservation and wise use of our common natural wealth. I know of no brighter constellation of devoted talent and high minded aim than that which unites the workers in the conservation field.

If these pages succeed in attracting to that field supporting strength my willing effort, in spite of its evident shortcomings, will not have been in vain.

*   *   *

My thanks are due to many friends for valuable advice. It is a long list and they will forgive me, I trust, if I do not list their names. Yet I feel that I should gratefully aknowledge the help extended to me, and mention those who actively assisted in the shaping of the book.

Foremost my associate of twenty-five years of happy and fruitful conservation labor, Stanley Coulter, Ph.D., LL.D.,

PREFACE

Sc.D., Dean of Men of Purdue University, now emeritus. Officers of the U. S. Department of the Interior, and of the U. S. Forest Service for many courtesies, maps and statistics included. Members of the National Resources Planning Board and staff members for source material and reading of chapters. Dr. Joseph S. Illick of Syracuse University for helpful criticism. Dr. John L. Bray of Purdue University for reading the chapter on Minerals. Mr. Robert Kingery for passing on Scenery. Professor Daniel DenUyl of Purdue University for valuable assistance with chapter on Forests. Mr. Ronald F. Lee, Chief, Branch of Historic Sites, National Park Service, for much detail in the collocation of the "Chronology"; Dr. Francis Ronalds for his initial furtherance of the plan. Messrs. Guy D. McKinney, Civilian Conservation Corps, and James F. Kieley, National Park Service, for notes and statistics on the Civilian Conservation Corps. Florence G. Ernsting for painstaking assistance.

Finally, I draw attention to the fact that for the sake of compactness of presentation, an important tabulation of all conservation acts in the United States ever passed in the forty-eight states had to be omitted. This highly useful work, to students as well as officials, done in the office of Mr. Roy A. Vetter, Associate Attorney, National Park Service, was taken over and published by the National Resources Planning Board as "State Planning—1942" and may be obtained from the Superintendent of Documents, Washington, D. C.

For kind permission to quote or reprint, thanks are due to the following:

The *American Mercury* (December, 1937), Paul B. Sears, "Death from the Soil."

PREFACE

The American Forestry Association, Ovid Butler, "American Conservation."

Harper's Magazine (May, 1940), John J. O'Neill, "Enter Atom Power."

Henry Holt and Company, Frederick Jackson Turner, *The Frontier in American History.*

Houghton Mifflin Company, Russell Lord, *Behold Our Land.*

Little, Brown and Company and the Atlantic Monthly Press, Burton J. Hendrick, *Bulwark of the Republic.*

The Macmillan Company, Charles Richard VanHise, *The Conservation of Natural Resources in the United States,* and Charles A. and Mary R. Beard, *The Rise of American Civilization.*

Meredith Nicholson, *The Provincial American.*

Louis B. Ward, M.A., Pd.M., "Business is Business." Pamphlet.

* * *

It seems fitting that I should close my book in the Hills o' Brown where I began it and, where long years ago I heard the call to bestir myself and build our Indiana State Parks.

Let that past be prologue, therefore, to my small but earnest effort. I know it would not have been made, nor other of my work in Parks and Conservation done without the faithful and intelligent support, sometimes alas with expostulative mien, of my boon companion on life's journey, my children's mother.

RICHARD LIEBER

Whip poor will Lodge
Brown County, Indiana
August 28, 1942

AMERICA'S NATURAL WEALTH

CHAPTER I

INTRODUCTION

W E IN this country are singularly blessed—blessed in
the wealth of our original natural resources; blessed,
too, in the fact that, in spite of our heedless waste and wanton abuse, we still have a sufficient store to maintain our
nation on a high level of prosperity—if only we awake to the
realization that the imperative need for conservation is
NOW!

Enlightened public opinion has been approaching this
realization—but not fast enough, or in sufficient numbers.
The aim of this book is to speed up this realization; to point
to the need for prompt, intelligent action on the part of all
our people, not just a few.

Conservation of our resources, both human and material,
touches all of us—in the lack or abundance of our food; in
the price we pay for clothes; in the availability of utilities;
in the luxury or poverty of our homes; in the health of our
bodies and of our communities; even in the weather.

We cannot continue to hide our heads in the sands of indifference and "let George do it." George too often has an
axe to grind; or is by nature self-interested; or, in the case
of official Georges, too hampered by outmoded legislation.

When we allow a large proportion of our coal to be lost
in the mining, we should know that we are wasting a vital,

1

irreplaceable resource which it took Nature ages to produce.

When we glut our streams with refuse and sewage, or build levees so the flood tide will pass our door, we should realize what is bound to happen downstream, and, in the last analysis, to all of us.

When we permit the ruthless destruction of our forests, we should know that we are removing the protection that our soil and water supply sorely needs, and laying the ground-work for new and ever increasing floods.

When, year after year, we allow soil to be leached out by single-cropping, we should realize that we are sowing the seeds for the same type of submarginal land production which brought poverty to China and other once prosperous nations.

Conservation is a vast subject with many ramifications, but a very concrete one as well. Tangible causes bring tangible, often visible, results. It is hoped that the evidence of our waste and abuse attested in the following pages will arouse a widespread desire to aid in their correction.

A study of conservation history will reveal that, although the approach by the various state governments was conspicuously haphazard, there has been a general trend in the direction of national action. It should be remembered in this connection that the states, not the Federal government, advanced the idea of Federal control, of a policy of comprehensive treatment of our natural resources. This desire, less altruistic than practical, follows the enlightening and often troublesome experience that oil and minerals, surface and underground waters, plant pests and diseases—to mention only a few of the items of conservation—are no respecters of artificial state boundaries.

INTRODUCTION

In the May, 1934, *Review of Reviews*, I submitted a statement that plans for social and economic reconstruction must include the orderly use of our national resources. It read in part as follows:

We are the most heedless and wasteful people on earth when it comes to use and appreciation of our inherited wealth in natural resources. . . .

We all know the story of national waste, beginning with the pioneer who in self-defense frequently had to waste, down to the present generation of exploiters, who—thanks to inefficient state and local government—still find things lying around loose. Neither are private exploiters the only agents of despoliation and destruction, aided by rotten political units and interminable delay in the courts.

Far from it. Lakes and rivers, natural assets of the first order, are used by cities large and small as open, running sewers. Lake and ocean fronts are used as political pawns. Natural and cultural development of the countryside is neglected, while underplanned and overbuilt cities are a menace and a challenge to our civilization.

At the time Theodore Roosevelt called the first White House Conference of Governors, and from then on, the gospel of conservation has been carried all over the land. It has made proselytes and apostles, camp followers, converts, and backsliders. Thanks to earnest leaders, it has left its impress on our times, if for nothing else than setting up and maintaining national danger signals. Within its own circles, it even has provoked bellicose conduct between groups of "conservationists," as they call themselves fervently though ungrammatically.

Bird-banding experts detest the duck hunter; nature-study folks lament the killing of quail; farmers oppose the deer as well as the deer slayer, and are up in arms against the "city sports" in general. Fox chasers would poison the fox hunters. Sportsmen of a sort expect a hundred dollars' worth of fish and game in return for a one-dollar license. Even fly casters and devotees of "nigger fishing" won't agree.

All that may be viewed in good humor and with charity, for it is all too human. Of much greater consequence is the large amount of waste in time and duplicated effort devoted to all phases of conservation. . . .

By and large, the conservation movement has remained one of academic and vocal significance, because real statesmen have failed to tie it up with our economic and social life. But there's the rub. What has the earnest conservator to show for twenty-five years of labor? Where, in the aggregate, does the movement stand today?

Why do we persist in ditching and draining the lakes and swamps —most glorious swamps at that—when we have more land than we know what to do with? Because somebody makes, or hopes to make, a profit from the sacrifices of public interest.

Why do our rivers continue to run like foul-smelling sewers? . . . Because habitual mismanagement of our cities, large and small, has stunted our civic sense until we are satisfied if filth and disease stop at our own threshold.

Why are forest fires, on top of the prodigal waste of lumbering and milling practices? Because we have "mined" timber, instead of guarding and holding it in sustained use.

Why do we shamelessly squander coal and oil and natural gas? Because we lack sane regulation. . . .

And so on, ad infinitum.

Have we given any consideration to balanced land utilization? Yes, we have begun timidly in larger cities with zoning plans. Perhaps that is a straw in the wind. What could you do, for instance, in a typical county with its opera-bouffe administration? Not much, I grant you. These counties, let alone the pathetic townships, are archaic relics, renowned in myth and saga and consequently heroically defended by the beneficiaries of their own maladministration.

The task of clean-cut land utilization transcends county and frequently state lines, just as these lines are non-existent in industrial, agricultural, financial, social, and cultural life.

What about our planless and wildly speculative extension of hydro-electric development? Is it not plain that the three great sources of mechanical power—coal, oil, and water—are in a death grapple for survival? Use and distribution of mechanical power should be one of the most powerful agencies for the advancement of human welfare. It should not be left to the gamblers in human happiness.

Why does all this continue when our best public opinion all these years has cried out against it? . . . Simply because we have no order in our public affairs, to enforce order.

The tenets of conservation are based on orderly procedure. Without the sun—the nourishment and protection of well-ordered government—they cannot thrive. They cannot even live where order is lacking.

The problem of conservation, of proper use of our natural resources, underlies our whole structure of social and economic organization. Yet natural resources in themselves would have no value unless they were used profitably and widely for the benefit of man. Theirs is the old story of the lump of gold on the desert island.

Natural resources today are being used by man, not wisely, but extravagantly and often destructively. This waste of all resources —land, waters, minerals and forests—has painfully impressed itself on the public mind, for its evil consequences are becoming more and more apparent.

In consequence, federal and state governments have enacted laws and more laws, have maintained "surveys," and have made progress in a limited way. They would have succeeded far better if the blight of partisan politics had not beset them.

But "politics," after all, is only concommitant with our national aversion to and suspicion of order. No other nation on earth could afford the politics we apparently enjoy. No other people would put up with waste, graft, incapacity, and disorder on our own grand scale.

Many conservators will agree that the complex problem of conservation can be solved only by first putting the house of government in order, be that federal, state, or even the lesser house of the locality.

Social justice and economic security demand a reorientation in production and distribution.

AMERICA'S NATURAL WEALTH

"We have the skill, we have the men, we have resources too," to paraphrase our cousins' boast of yesteryear. We are rich as a nation, very rich, present difficulties notwithstanding. All we need is leadership, common-sense direction, and consequently a better order.

Today we are far from having that essential basis to work upon. The world over, governments have fallen, not so much on account of their inherent faults as on account of the incapacity or unwillingness of their leaders to modernize governmental machinery. The people have lost faith. Desperate people have made desperate changes, for what has evolved in many lands is far from promising. Yet it is a groping for better order. No government can endure without order. . . .

Since when was popular government imperiled by adaptation to its own new order? The danger to free institutions lies exactly in the opposite direction, that of obstinate insistence on the status quo. . . .

If we want to save and maintain the lofty (and workable) ideals of civil liberty, we must have better social and administrative order. Above all, we must advance in the spirit of "life, liberty and the pursuit of happiness" until we have crowned the work of the fathers with the institution of Economic Liberty.

Can we do it? Of course we can. Nothwithstanding the past gruesome waste, our natural resources, the basis of all comfort and prosperity, are still enormous. The wealth in minerals, in soil, in the fortunately replaceable values of timber, make us not only rich in quantity but also in variety. Our knowledge of natural sciences and their application to technological advancement has opened an almost unlimited vista of progress.

The natural sciences have performed a modern miracle. They have taught us how best to use resources, and how to transform them. But, in the nature of things, we must leave it to organized society to distribute these gains more equitably.

As a people, what have we so far done? We have elected a leader to clean up the wreckage and put new order into things. Through

INTRODUCTION

Congress we gave him extraordinary powers, for we were badly scared.

Since that time the President, confronted by an almost super-human task, has labored ceaselessly and with rare good judgment at preliminaries, first to stop the conflagration, and secondly to recover the salvage. This latter is the phase we are in today.

Next, we hope, will come his permanent plans of nation-wide reconstruction on the foundation of a better social, political, and economic order. It will be the President's task to formulate these plans and submit them to the people for their acceptance. Irrespective of partisan politics, the people will follow the President in his determination to rid the country of political "blocs," of private graft and waste, and save it for popular government.

Such a comprehensive program must needs concern itself with our national resources and their manifold uses: land, water, forests, and minerals.

An extensive amount of rich study material has been developed in the last twenty-five years; also a certain amount of success as well as failure. Might it not be helpful to the President, fitting conservation into his greater plans, to furnish him with—

First: A succinct résumé of the gains of conservation for the stated period.

Second: A statement of present-day failure and reasons why.

Third: A tabulation of our natural resources by states.

Fourth: A study of present use, distribution, and consumption.

Fifth: A study of waste and by-products.

Sixth: A study of land utilization, in all of its applications: industrial, agricultural, urban, rural, scenic, sylvicultural, waters and waterways, educational and cultural.

Such an enumeration would disclose the importance of our natural resources as well as their relation to our whole national economy. It would give the government the facts on which to base all manner of state aid in the future.

Should the President see fit to entrust this all-important charge to his competent Secretary of the Interior, conservation of our natural resources would immediately be lifted from its academic and experimental stage to a new state of functioning, with all its dynamic force in full play, for the achievement of a higher life, a more genuine liberty, and a finer pursuit of happiness.

Much to my gratification, the President in July, 1934, by executive order established the National Resources Board, absorbing both the National Planning Board and the Committee on National Land Problems.

This Board consisted of the Secretary of the Interior, as Chairman, the Secretaries of War, of Agriculture, of Commerce, and of Labor, and Messrs. Frederic A. Delano, Charles E. Merriam, and Wesley C. Mitchell. It was directed to prepare and present to the President a program and plan of procedure dealing with the physical, social, governmental, and economic aspects of public policies for the development and use of land, water, and other natural resources and related subjects. In the short years of its existence, this Board did an enormous amount of work in the indicated direction.

In June, 1935, this Board became the National Resources Committee, with only slightly altered responsibilities. On July 1, 1939, under Reorganization Plan No. 1, the functions of the Committee were merged with those of the Employment Stabilization Office, established under the Employment Stabilization Act of 1931, and the reorganized unit, under the name of the National Resources Planning Board,[1] was made a unit within the Executive Office of the President. Its functions and activities are as follows:

1. To collect, prepare, and make available to the Presi-

[1] In the following pages, in order to avoid obfuscation owing to its frequent changes in name, the present appelation of National Resources Planning Board is used. This method seems appropriate because its functions though enlarged since 1934 remain the same in principle.

INTRODUCTION

dent such plans, data, and information as may be helpful to
a planned development and use of national resources, and
related subjects referred to it by the President, and to recommend to the President and the Congress long-time plans
and programs for the wide use and fullest development of
such resources.

2. To advise the President from time to time of the trend
of employment and business activity, and of the existence or
approach of periods of business depression and unemployment in the United States or in any substantial portion
thereof; and to recommend measures leading to the improvement and stabilization of economic conditions.

3. To collect information concerning advance construction plans and estimates of all Federal agencies, the agencies
of the states and municipalities, and other public and private
agencies, and to list for the President and the Congress all
proposed public works in the order of their relative importance with respect to (a) the greatest good of the greatest
number of people; (b) the emergency necessities of the nation; and (c) the social, economic, and cultural advancement of the people of the United States.

4. To receive and record all proposed Federal projects
involving the acquisition of land (including transfer of land
jurisdiction) and land-research projects, and, in an advisory
capacity, to provide the agencies concerned with such information or data as may be pertinent to the projects.

5. To consult and co-operate with agencies of the Federal
government, with the states and municipalities or agencies
thereof, and with any public or private planning or research
agencies or institutions, in carrying out any of its duties
and functions, and to act as a clearinghouse and means of

9

co-ordination for planning activities, linking together various levels and fields of planning.

But the National Resources Planning Board is only a planning, surveying, and investigating agency—not an executive one. What is needed further is a branch of the government carrying out the policy of conservation through functional subdivisions.

The work of conservation to be effective must be united. Today it is not. What we have of it is scattered among several departments and bureaus. Under such circumstances there can be no comprehensive view of or action on the conservation of our natural resources in their totality. For intelligent action we must have a better knowledge of our resources, and no one should be more interested in this than the Federal government itself, for it owns approximately 400,000,000 acres of land—about one-fourth of the country's total area.

The President some time ago appointed a committee to investigate the matter of governmental reorganization. Their report included a proposal for a Department of Conservation. *All conservation matters belong in one department!* Such a department not only would administer all laws primarily concerned with the conservation of natural resources, but it would have the following results:

1. It would recognize the conservation of natural resources as one of the major functions of government, giving it a firmer position in the minds of the people and of those who make and administer our laws.

2. It would give the people a spokesman in the President's cabinet, named for his interest in and knowledge of conservation; it would also establish standards by which both ap-

pointments and policies would be tested in the public mind.

3. It would give a much closer tie between Federal and state conservation work, since activities which now touch the states in many lines, often in conflict, would be brought together under a single head.

4. Conservation agencies would be freed from conflicting controls in the various departments among which they are now scattered, and these departments in turn would be freed from work which does not belong in, but hampers the discharge of, their functional duties.

5. Under a Department of Conservation, there could be a balanced and co-ordinated administration of forests, recreation, wildlife, grazing, water, and mineral resources, each receiving proper emphasis in the national economy.

The existing disorganization in Federal conservation work is defeating the purposes for which the work was undertaken. As long as conservation agencies are farmed out like so many orphans, scattered throughout the government departments, they will either be neglected as orphans, or be subject to the demoralizing rivalries and jealousies of their various guardians. Once again, conservation, as Van Hise pointed out long ago, "is not a simple subject which can be treated with reference to a single resource independently of others; it is an interlocking one. The conservation of one resource is related to that of another."

Under our present antiquated machinery, conservation can only be attempted piecemeal, and even that breaks down in the rivalries between departments. Conflicting and overlapping jurisdictions, bureaucratic jealousies, waste and inefficiency characterize the present chaotic arrangement, or lack of arrangement.

11

Let me give you a brief résumé of the situation as described in the report of a committee appointed by the President to investigate the matter of governmental reorganization. This report, which included a proposal for a Department of Conservation, shows how badly needed are greater harmony, order, efficiency, and economy in government.

THE EXECUTIVE'S WORKSHOP

Article 2, Section 3 of the Constitution of the United States prescribes, "He (the President) shall from time to time give to the Congress information on the state of the Union and recommend to their consideration such measures as he shall judge necessary and expedient. . . ."

In order to discharge this duty intelligently, the President must have knowledge of all of the facts. As the government's administrative management has developed from the beginning, it is an impossibility for the President to know all the facts. As a result, "neither the President nor the Congress can exercise effective supervision and direction over such a chaos of establishments, nor can overlapping, duplication and contradictory policies be avoided."

The need for this information is very great, for without proper information the people will not be enabled to concentrate upon essentials. David Cushman Coyle has put this need in terse language:

The average American citizen has not the time nor the inclination to read scientific reports or lengthy government documents or economic books of a kind to explain everything to him . . . those who are in charge of our government have got to look more in the future than they ever have in the past to that function which is stated in

12

the Constitution as the duty of the Executive to report to the American people on the state of the nation. That is, they must be told what they are up against. They must be told the major items about what this country is all about and where we stand and where we are headed; so that in the main the people, who, after all, can see a barn door if it is in front of their noses, will know what these things are. And the major part of this process consists, I believe, in educating the American people to visualize our whole country as our estate which we are supposed to take care of.

As matters stand, the Chief Executive frequently is Chief Executive in name only. It is a public secret that with the present administrative setup for the executive branch the President is constantly overworked and overwhelmed with the flood of detail "arising directly from the bad organization and equipment of the government." There exist, unbelievable as it is, over one hundred independent agencies, administrations, authorities, boards, and commissions, often unrelated and certainly not subordinated to those executives directly responsible to the President.

The independent commissions present a serious immediate problem. No administrative reorganization worthy of the name can leave hanging in the air more than a dozen powerful, irresponsible agencies free to determine policy and administer law.

Congress is always tempted to turn each new regulatory function over to a new independent commission. This is not only following the line of least resistance; it is also following a fifty-year-old tradition. The multiplication of these agencies cannot fail to obstruct the effective over-all management of the executive branch of the government almost in geometric ratio to their number. At the present rate, we shall have forty to fifty of them within a decade. Every bit of executive and administrative authority which they enjoy means a relative weakening of the President, in whom, according to the Constitution, "the executive power shall be vested." As they grow in number, his stature is bound to diminish. He will no longer be in reality the Executive, but only one of many executives, threading his way around obstacles which he has no power to overcome.

We have watched the growth of boards and commissions transform the executive branches of our state governments into grotesque agglomerations of independent and irresponsible units, bogged down by the weight and confusion of the whole crazy structure. The same tendency in national administration will bring the same disastrous results. That tendency should be stopped.

The Brownlow Committee, appointed by the President, made a report on better administrative management. Its proposals may be stated under five major points and may be summarized as follows:

1. Expand the White House staff so that the President may have a sufficient group of able assistants in his own office to keep him in closer and easier touch with the widespread affairs of administration and to make a speedier clearance of the knowledge needed for executive decision.

2. Strengthen and develop the managerial agencies of the government, particularly those dealing with the budget, efficiency research, personnel, and planning, as management arms of the Chief Executive.

3. Extend the merit system upward, outward, and downward to cover all non-policy-determining posts; reorganize the civil service system as a part of management under a

14

single responsible administrator, strengthening the Civil Service Commission as a citizens' civil service board to serve as the watchdog of the merit system; and increase the salaries of key posts throughout the service so that the government may attract and hold in a career service men and women of the highest ability and character.

4. Overhaul the one hundred independent agencies, administrations, authorities, boards, and commissions, and place them by executive order within one or the other of the following twelve major executive departments: State, Treasury, War, Justice, Post Office, Navy, Conservation, Agriculture, Commerce, Labor, Social Welfare, and Public Works; place upon the executive continuing responsibility for the maintenance of effective organization.

5. Establish accountability of the Executive to the Congress by providing a genuine independent post audit of all fiscal transactions by an auditor general, and restore to the Executive complete responsibility for accounts and current financial transactions.

As a nation we have outgrown the facilities both in methods and equipment of a bygone day. "The executive structure of the government is sadly out of date," said President Roosevelt. "I am not the first President to report to the Congress that antiquated machinery stands in the way of effective administration and of adequate control by the Congress. Theodore Roosevelt, William Howard Taft, Woodrow Wilson, and Herbert Hoover made repeated but not wholly successful efforts to deal with the problems. Committees of the Congress have also rendered distinguished service to the nation through their efforts from time to time to point the way to improvement of government management and organization." The President continued, "In these troubled years of world history, a self-government cannot long survive unless that government is an effective and efficient agency to serve mankind and carry out the will of the nation. A government without good management is a house builded on sand."

Notwithstanding the intent of the Constitution, we find in reality that the effectiveness of the Chief Executive is limited and restricted, for how can it be humanly possible for him to "know fully the affairs and problems of over a hundred separate major agencies, to say nothing of being responsible for their general direction and co-ordination"? A strong presentation is made by the President's committee on the inadequacy of the executive branch of the government. It says:

The structure of the government throws an impossible task upon the Chief Executive. No President can possibly give adequate supervision to the multitude of agencies which have been set up to carry on the work of the government, nor can he co-ordinate their activities and policies.

The normal managerial agencies designed to assist the Executive in thinking, planning, and managing, which one would expect to find in any large-scale organization, are either undeveloped or lacking.

The constitutional principle of the separation of powers and the responsibility of the President for the "executive power" is impaired through the multiplicity and confusion of agencies which render effective action impossible.

Without plan or intent, there has grown up a headless "fourth branch" of the government, responsible to no one, and impossible of co-ordination with the general policies and work of the government as determined by the people through their duly elected representatives. . . .

INTRODUCTION

Owing to the multiplicity of agencies and the lack of administrative management, there is waste, overlapping and duplication, which may be eliminated through co-ordination, consolidation, and proper managerial control.

The greatest and most important corporation in the United States is the United States government itself. It affects the well-being of every citizen. It employs far more people than the greatest industrial corporation. How it manages to get along at all is the marvel of all ages. No commercial organization could hope to prosper or even survive under similar management. The time and energy wasted these many years because of departmental jealousies would have sufficed to build up powerful commercial and industrial institutions.

The whole thing doesn't make good service or good sense.

I have mentioned the hundred or more non-subordinated agencies. Would it surprise the reader to learn how these departments and agencies for their purposes subdivide the country into regions? Some one hundred and nine different plans of geographical subdivision of the United States are used by the various government agencies. In place of that, the administrative work of the executive branch should be carried on by a few regional units each set up to cover all the work contemplated for its region. In this manner the government would not only be brought in closer touch with the people, but it would the better co-operate with state and local governments in consequence.

Indeed it is true, as the committee reports, that—

the structure as it now stands is inefficient; it is a poor instrument for rendering public service; and it thwarts democratic control. With such a planless organization, good management is almost impossible—a fact of great importance in the modern world in which nothing can continue without good management, not even democracy.

In order to improve the mechanics, the committee recommended twelve departments to constitute the operating division of the executive branch of the Federal government. Approving this plan, President Roosevelt pointed out that the reduction from one hundred down to a dozen operating executive agencies would have the wholesome effect of bringing many little bureaucracies under broad, co-ordinated, democratic authority. In so doing, he said, "we shall know that we are going back to the Constitution and giving to the executive branch modern tools of management and up-to-date organization which will enable the government to go forward efficiently. We can prove to the world that American government is both democratic and efficient."

In conclusion, the President's committee has this to say:

Good management will promote in the fullest measure the conservation and utilization of our national resources, and spell this out plainly in social justice, security, order, liberty, prosperity, in material benefits, and in higher values of life. The adjustments and arrangements we suggest have no other purpose or justification than better public service for our people through better administrative management.

At the close of the Seventy-Fifth Congress, Third Session, a reorganization bill failed of passage in the House through recommitment to committee. Opponents of the bill consisted of two widely divergent groups: one fearful that this particular bill would give the President almost dictatorial power; the other group largely guided by the fear that their

18

own importance in government would be reduced. One can
understand the attitude of the former, which is not only
legitimate but patriotic—if they should be right in their
contention. That of the latter is indefensible from any standpoint.

The situation has been made worse because our present-
day government, under the stress of time, had to undertake
many functions which resulted in the multiplication of
bureaus and agencies. Some of these have been placed within
existing departments, others have received independent
status. Their tendency is to wax powerful and reach out for
additional functions not contemplated in their creation.
Overlapping and fruitless duplication is the order of the day.
Within the purview of our particular consideration comes
the management of our natural resources. Conservation of
the natural wealth is but one of the many items in the national economy. In its proper relation to all of these varied
objects, it nevertheless, for the sake of order, should be so set
aside as the fountainhead of its own proper function as to be
able at all times, as a unit, to co-operate with and support
any one or more of the other projected departments in their
particular activities.

Today we are far from that common-sense attitude. There
exist endless chances for conflict, and these have led to rivalries and controversy between bureaus competing for jurisdiction over the same subjects. In fact, this sort of thing has
gone so far that we see competition between bureaus belong-
ing to the same department. It is a wild scramble for expansion of power, a negation of the very principle of conservation, and insistence upon costly duplication by way of
particularistic function.

This is an issue far transcending the petty quarrels of government bureaus or the rivalries of existing departments. The time has come to build for the future. The proper use of our natural resources has a vital bearing upon economic and social organization in the United States. We cannot afford to continue either the senseless squandering of natural riches that has marked our growth as a nation, or the waste and decay caused by failure to make wise use of what is left. Such use and adequate protection can only be guaranteed under comprehensive policies within one department, and that department designated by name—so that every man, woman, and child may understand its purpose, and every government employee may feel the weight of the words— Department of Conservation.

Conservation is not a function but a principle. If conservation as a principle is going to live, it must have a fountainhead from which functions are delegated to replace the present system in which each little fountainhead issuing forth as a small stream imagines itself to be a big river, and, in its peripatetic course, tries to find its own separate outlet to the sea of public service.

Not long ago *The Sphere* had this to say about us and our national feasting:

The United States contains six per cent of the world's area and seven per cent of its population. It normally consumes forty-eight per cent of the world's rubber, twenty-one per cent of its sugar, seventy-two per cent of its silk, thirty-six per cent of its coal, forty-two per cent of its pig iron, forty-seven per cent of its copper, and sixty-nine per cent of its crude petroleum.

The United States operates sixty per cent of the world's telephone and telegraph facilities, owns eighty per cent of the motor cars in use, operates thirty-three per cent of the railroads. It produces seventy per cent of the oil, sixty per cent of the wheat and cotton, fifty per cent of the copper and pig iron, and forty per cent of the lead and coal output of the globe.

The United States possesses almost $11,000,000,000 (now 24 billion dollars) in gold, or nearly half of the world's monetary metal. It has two-thirds of civilization's banking resources. The purchasing power of the population is greater than that of the 400,000,000 people in Europe and much larger than that of the more than a billion Asiatics.

Responsible leadership which cannot translate such a bulging economy into assured prosperity is destitute of capacity. But pompous statesmen, looking over the estate, solemnly declare that the methods by which it was created are all wrong, ought to be abandoned, must be discarded, and that the time has come to substitute political management for individual initiative and supervision.

There is only one way to characterize that proposal—it is just damn foolishness.

To which the Scripps-Howard press replied:

It is well for the writer to remind us of our great wealth and our great opportunity.

But never have we heard anyone declare that the methods by which our wealth was created were all wrong. For it was created by Nature, which prepared the resources of a vast continent.

Then individual initiative began to create. It created ways of exploiting those resources. Some of the ways were good. Many of them were reckless, wasteful, greedy.

And then political management, as the only management capable of representing all of the people, had to step in. That political management has made mistakes is certain. It would be foolish to turn everything over to political management, as it would be foolish to turn everything back to individual initiative.

What is needed is that these two—government and business— shall work together to develop ways of husbanding and using our resources for the benefit of all the people. Only so can our wealth mean assured prosperity. If they will not work together, if they persist in fighting, poverty in the midst of plenty will continue. For that, indeed, will America deserve to be accused of damn foolishness.

So while the tug of war between conflicting viewpoints continues, the practical distance between our potential feasting and famine decreases daily. Enlightened public opinion must step forward. For the safety of our nation and its lofty principles, there is no longer any room for *laissez faire* attitudes. Waiting for mass conscience, mass judgment, mass responsibility to assert itself is futile. By and large, there is no such thing. As always we must continue to depend upon devoted, inspired, and high-minded individuals for our salvation in such matters.

No nation can stand still. It must advance or die. As Americans we know only how to advance.

CHAPTER II

NATURAL RESOURCES—THE BASIS OF AMERICAN WEALTH

MORE than a century after the discovery of the New World, the Virginia Capes and Plymouth Rock saw the beginning of the occupation and conquest of the present territory of the United States.

Europeans colonized the country, but America made the American what he is today.

Synchronous with the Declaration of Independence was James Watt's steam engine, which harnessed resource energy and changed the aspect of civilization. On the one hand, a declaration of political independence; on the other, an instrument for the attainment of economic independence. A newly established government in a new land filled with basic wealth had only to call upon the services of the awakening giant, Power, to start it on the high road of industrial supremacy.

As a nation we have been singularly fortunate. We have attained our present standing in the front rank of nations for three reasons: First, geographical position; second, natural wealth; and, third, courage, hard work, and never-failing ingenuity, especially with respect to mechanical appliances, in harnessing and using power.

We have all that—an excellent arrangement of seaports, of plains, rivers, lakes large and small, hills and mountains.

We have practically all the natural resources we need, plus the necessary amount of intelligence to direct the work. Natural wealth is the source of our prosperity and the basis of our national institutions. We must find food, shelter, and clothing for the millions of our people, in order first to safeguard and next to raise the standards of our social, intellectual, artistic, and ethical achievements.

"It is the purpose of conservation," said Van Hise, "to reduce the intensity of the struggle for existence; to make the situation more favorable; to reduce mere subsistence to a subordinate place, and thus give an opportunity for development to a higher intellectual and spiritual level."

Unfortunately, we have carried on a terrific waste in nearly every direction. In the three hundred years of our occupation of this marvelous land, we have wasted much outright and ruined as much indirectly.

The first onslaught was made against the fur-bearing animals. Much as we deplore this destruction, there was no moral turpitude involved in its practice, for the number of the fur-bearers seemed inexhaustible. Besides, no one in particular enforced claim to them or to their habitat.

The next attack was against the forests, necessarily so in the beginning, perhaps, but it did not stop when it should have stopped. Lumbering began near the Atlantic, moved west, and has not as yet quite ruined the country in its last stand in Oregon, Washington, and California.

The thought of conservation is comparatively new. It marks a new era in the development of the country, and nowhere are its lessons more needed than in a country like ours, vast in its expanse, relatively sparsely populated, and apparently inexhaustible in its natural riches.

But are these riches inexhaustible? Can we go on in the manner of our fathers and forefathers, who frequently had to destroy in self-defense?

That the pioneer, coming to this land, was destructive before he could be constructive is a matter of historical truth. It could not have been otherwise. He fought civilization's battle that civilization may enjoy peace and prosperity. But some of these destructive habits of the settler have taken root, and destruction has continued where construction was needed. As a people we have wasted land and water, fish and game, coal, natural gas, and too many other riches.

From the sun and from the earth, the one the provider and the other the common mother, come our very life. This one fact, at least, must be clear to all, to the thinker as well as the toiler, to the grateful and careful user as well as to the most prodigal despoiler and reckless exploiter of her bounty. The earth, down to the deepest mine, every drop of water in her lakes, seas, and rivers, the air itself which sweeps and energizes all things—these are not only our living abode, not only our last resting place, but the source of our maintenance, our happiness, and prosperity. Like a living mother the earth keeps a well-filled larder of wonderful variety to gratify our needs, our comforts, even our whims and the desire for luxuries. The earth is our common mother and her riches, therefore, belong commonly to all her children.

But unlike his diminishing dependence on natural parents, in spite of great development and progress, man has remained dependent upon the earth. He fell heir to a country incomparably richer than that on which the messengers of Moses reported, but what use has he made of it?

In the seventies of the last century, it was realized by scientists that our timber supply had been dangerously reduced. Subsequently, a need for irrigation was felt, and simultaneously, a close connection between forest and water resources was discovered.

The American waste of coal, both in the process of mining and in the method of use, is equally ruthless. We have poisoned our landscapes by turning our rivers into open running sewers. We have wasted wantonly that most precious and perfect fuel, natural gas. Horrible examples in profusion are not lacking, but in general the one form of waste to strike popular imagination has been the destruction of our forests.

There was a time when sections of land, mines, and forests could be had from the government for the asking, but that time is long past. All of these vast resources which we thought unlimited are found not to be inexhaustible. Not only is the quantity of many of these natural resources reduced, but there is continued pressure to take what is left in the hands of the government and place it in those of private persons or corporations.

The very aspect of American scenery is being changed. Uncontrolled fires have swept through our forests. In one year, in Minnesota, a district half again as large as the state of Massachusetts was burned over. Erosion has set in. Silt is filling in rivers. Hydro-electric developments scar the countryside, and while trying to extract wealth from "white coal" the promoters themselves are in danger of annihilation by the very natural forces whose balances they have upset and which now are filling these reservoirs, euphemistically called lakes, with steadily gaining sediment.

Not only are the sources of mechanical power—coal, oil, and water—wastefully treated, but in some cases, such as oil-drilling regulations, we have actually put a premium on waste. It took forty-four years up to 1900 to produce one billion barrels of oil in the United States. Now we consume this quantity in a year and a quarter. So far as coal is concerned, we find that initial conservation of the resource would demand better and safer mining. A reduction of from fifty to ten per cent of operating waste should be obtained. Beyond that there is further need of conservation by providing better firing methods, increasing thermal units, and decreasing smoke nuisance, with all its attendant waste of and damage to life and property.

The bituminous coal industry, economically one of the most important, is in a state of vast disorder. The moment the price of steam coal goes over a certain maximum in cost, a maximum much too low to provide living conditions for miners, electricity takes it place, while oil enters whenever the two other powers fail to reach a maximum of performance.

Only now is it being borne home to us that natural resources provide our prosperity, our strength, perhaps the very seeds of our life and independence, as we realize more and more clearly that the present cyclopean struggle is not so much a matter of opposing ideologies—in its present vague sense—as it is one for the possession of coveted natural resources.

Our natural wealth has a direct bearing upon our natural security and prosperity, upon civic and political betterment, and finally upon individual happiness. The time has come to arouse the fighting spirit of intelligent laymen on behalf of the cause of national conservation. It is today one of the most active forces for human betterment. Daily we are seeing more and more clearly that, in addition to our individual happiness and security, the stability of our national institutions depends upon our vast national wealth and its proper use.

It depends on the steps we take today whether America will continue to be a land of promise tomorrow.

1. MINERALS

CHAPTER III

THE LIFEBLOOD OF OUR POWER AGE

TODAY we are living out of the past—out of the countless aeons of time during which we were building up our vast stores of mineral wealth. When we burn coal, petroleum, or gasoline, we release and put to our use the energy of the sun stored in plants millions of years ago. These resources differ from water and vegetation, which are, generally speaking, self-renewing, in that they are non-renewable and not inexhaustible.

"Our power age," it has been said, "is a continuous roar of plant explosion of buried sun power."

Written history and monuments go back about sixty-two centuries. During sixty and one-half of these centuries, all labor was performed either by man or beast. Small wonder that we cling to the expression "horse power" for measuring mechanical power. It has been only during the last brief century that the expansion of natural sciences and the development of technology have changed the world into what it is today, a world where the labor of man or beast is being consistently shifted onto a machine driven by mechanical power.

The oldest living things in our country are the big trees in California, *Sequoia gigantea*, variously estimated at from three thousand to five thousand years old. But even these are unborn infants as compared with the hoary age of our mineral and soil resources.

31

So time becomes the very core of the problem. Time was. conceived by Pythagoras, according to Plutarch, as the soul of the world. Does time exist at all? We may assert, but cannot prove, its existence. All we can do is to find a mode of relating external objects with sensation.

Geologists, physicists, biologists, and paleontologists, concerned with the stuff of the universe out of which was derived our solar system, speak in terms of hundreds of millions of years. They try to apprehend the approximate development of the earth during its cooling process. They study volcanic action, and the nature of the rocks derived from it. Igneous rocks, the action of ice, falling water and rising vapors, the solidification of metals—to speak only of a few of the many actors on the stage of creation—hold their rapt attention, with the result that increase of knowledge, or at least acceptance of scientific theories, has vastly elongated the length of creation periods over what previously had been accepted.

How can we comprehend the span of such mighty ages? The answer, of course, is that most of us cannot do so. These concepts are too big for us. The findings of science remain miracles which we do not attempt to comprehend, until advancing technology transforms them into articles of daily use. Then the miracle becomes commonplace. Yet the radio and the automobile still remain, to some extent, miracles.

Russell Lord, in his book *Behold Our Land*, has conceived a most ingenious way of making clear to us just what three-quarters of a billion years means. He uses a time-lapse picture analogy. Briefly sketched, this is the gist of his fascinating presentation:

Some of us have seen time-lapse pictures in which, in a few minutes on the screen, is shown the life-span of a tree: how the seeds

32

sprout, put forth leaves, develop stems and blossoms, and bear fruit. This is done by setting the camera to take one exposure, say, every fifteen seconds. This would make two hundred and forty exposures per hour; projected on the screen at the usual rate of twenty-four frames a second, the film would show an hour's growth in ten seconds, a day's growth in four minutes, and so forth.

We shall now put our imagination to work and fancy that there was in that beginning of things a machine set by providence, let us say on the moon, automatically so regulated as to take one shot per year. That is, in twenty-four years twenty-four exposures. Projected at a normal rate, such a film would show twenty-four years of change in a second; 1,440 years of change in a minute; 86,400 years of change in an hour; 2,000,000 years of change in a day; 757,000,000 years of change in a year.

Now let us suppose that this time-lapse film is brought to earth for showing in some great hall. It will take a full year, in fact a leap year, day and night, to run this entire film. As the scene opens, the earth writhes and heaves as though in monstrous labor, with no living thing in view. We see shore lines change, mountains and uplands rear, rivers seek the sea again, sediments change into rock or compact strata. Day and night the picture grinds on.

In March, the story has advanced to 568,000,000 years ago.

On July 1, it is 360,000,000 years ago. For the first time vegetation appears. The earth puts on verdure and is covered. The soil begins to hold more water. In July, limbless vertebrates appear in the waters.

By August, some 300,000,000 years ago, amphibians have come ashore.

In September, we see the first reptiles and primitive insects. At about the same time, some 250,000,000 years in the past, the sea again laps over the greater part of North America and, retreating, lays under swamps enormous deposits of carbonized vegetation— now mined as coal.

October brings on the dinosaurs and the first mammals. By mid-October birds and flying reptiles appear.

33

AMERICA'S NATURAL WEALTH

Early in November, we have to account for only 150,000,000 years from the present day.

We are now in December, the last month of its showing. We have 62,000,000 years still ahead of us. The Himalayas, Alps, Rockies, and Andes are to be made and remade. Around noon, December 31, man first gets into the picture. Life is decidedly in the raw; glaciers and sweeping climatic changes keep man constantly on the move. This marching ice had its own way in Europe and particularly in North America.

There come now the last five minutes of our picture. At 11:55 we see the world 7,200 years ago; at 11:59 it is anno Domini 496. The story has been running for one year, day and night, and the last minute of the film ticks off everything that has happened from 496 to date. Roughly speaking, it includes, therefore, everything in human history and experience from the end of the Roman Empire to the beginning of the New Deal. The entire time of civilized man, the world over, is somewhere between three and four minutes. The time of American civilization, in these terms, is less than twenty seconds.

Let us look closely at the last minute. Its first twenty seconds show the world overrun by barbarian hordes; the Crusades begin and end; the long boats of the Norsemen and others explore the seas. At the forty-first second, Columbus touches North America. At the forty-sixth second, Jamestown is founded. At the fifty-third second, we fight the British. Even this late in the story, the film only four or five seconds from its ending, the territory of the United States stretches westward, still a virgin country. Thus, in a little more than a hundred years (four or five seconds at the showing) the United States is transformed into the greatest industrial and commercial power in the world. There never has been anything like this in all the history of earth or man.

Today we live in a power age surrounded by machines. Both power and machines are derived from minerals. Yet most of us hardly recognize the presence and influence of minerals, although our whole existence is dependent upon

34

them and their proper utilization. They are the lifeblood of our entire power-age economy.

Throughout man's history, minerals have played an important part in the rise of civilization and culture. Classical mythology divided the world's history into a Golden Age, a Silver Age, a Bronze Age, and an Iron Age. Modern archaeologists speak of the Old Stone Age, the New Stone Age, the Bronze Age, and the Iron Age.

Archaeologists show that all human development—social, cultural, political, and economic—is based on the abundance and variety of material resources. They reveal that mankind, by his appropriation and use of his mineral resources, beginning with the stone hammer and progressing to the transatlantic clipper, has really managed to "go places," no doubt in spite of the prevailing attitude described in these cogent lines by Charlotte Perkins Gilman:

There was once a Neolithic man, an enterprising wight,
Who made his chopping implements unusually bright.
Unusually clever he, unusually brave,
And he drew delightful Mammoths on the borders of his cave.
To his Neolithic neighbors, who were startled and surprised,
Said he, "My friends, in course of time, we shall be civilized!
We are going to live in cities! We are going to fight in wars!
We are going to eat three times a day without the natural cause!
We are going to turn life upside down about a thing called gold!
We are going to want the earth, and take as much as we can hold!
We are going to wear great piles of stuff outside our proper skins!
We are going to have Diseases! And Accomplishments!! and Sins!!!"

It is a far cry from the caveman's maul to the armored motor tank of today. The story of these aeons of forgotten time reads more like a romance than a sober research into the history of man. It is especially interesting to observe that original uses of stone, metals, or alloys have, in their survival, shown a remarkable resistance to obsolescence. We still use rotary millstones invented in the Bronze Age. We still depend upon bronze for bells, statues, and ornaments. We could not do without the wheel, also a product of the Bronze Age.

For weal or woe humanity has always depended on the use of its mineral resources in its struggle for existence. This dependence was never greater than it is in our modern age of power in which minerals supply ninety per cent of the national requirements for mechanical energy—the remaining ten per cent being delivered by water—and in which the machine using the power is of mineral origin as well.

No country in the world can match us in the variety and abundance of our minerals. From our great national storehouse—the earth—we provide nearly half of the total value of the entire world's mineral production. We produce nearly half of the mechanical energy of the entire world. Minerals represent about forty per cent of the total value of all our own great natural resources. Second only to agriculture, their production in 1940 had a value close to $5,582,500,000.

Let us take a brief look backward at what mechanical power has done for us and to us. Within a century and a half, man has stepped into a new era. He left the Iron Age with the first piston stroke of Watt's steam engine and found himself in a new world of seemingly unlimited possibilities. Humanitarians saw mankind released from drudgery. Reformers promised liberty, prosperity, and education for all. Both had great hope, but neither could afford to make promises, for the power was not in their control. Those who possessed it made brutally selfish use of it, as illustrated by the early English factory system. In spite of all that, including present-day social injustices and economic imbecilities, living conditions of the mass of the people are vastly higher than they ever have been before. So far as the enjoyment of bodily comfort is concerned, no country ranks higher than ours. Consider that the average American possesses an automobile —a truck or a tractor if on a farm; a washing machine; an electric iron; a fan and a toaster; a vacuum cleaner, a telephone, a gas or electric range, heat, light, and finally a radio.

There are, in this country, 32,452,861 (1940 registration) automobiles, as opposed to 12,969,550 for the rest of the world; 28,000,000 radio sets in homes, not counting those in automobiles and elsewhere. It is estimated that there are in domestic use 7,000,000 mechanical refrigerators, 10,-000,000 vacuum cleaners, washing machines, and electric toasters, and twice that number of electric irons.

Not all of our fellow men, unfortunately, enjoy these great blessings. True patriotism, love for our fellow men, as well as common sense, demand that all gains be converted into mass gains. If we accept the present estimates of ten horse power available per person in the United States, it means that each person would have the incredible mechanical equivalent of no less than four hundred slaves at his beck and call, doing what never could have been done by hand alone.

CHAPTER IV

LIVING OUT OF PRINCIPAL

THE American consumer has been furnished the cheapest fuel and some of the cheapest metal in the world. The output per miner in the United States is far higher than that in foreign countries. A ton of soft coal in America requires 1.7 hours of labor; in England, 7.5 hours. As a result of lesser production, the British miner is paid less for his labor and the British consumer pays more for his coal.

In the first half of the last century, the United Kingdom led in the production of coal, iron, copper, lead, zinc, and tin. There are still ample reserves, but the increasing difficulty of extraction has become so great that the mining of copper and zinc has practically been abandoned.

This experience is of interest to us because it presages a condition that, in time, will face our nation. It indicates a cost rising out of all proportion after the deposits within easy reach have been depleted. Though the British reserve of coal is still ninety-three per cent against seven per cent removal, depths as great as 3,700 feet have been reached in order to mine this seven per cent. What will be the expense of extracting the remaining ninety-three per cent?

Our problem, therefore, is not to await the day—perhaps centuries hence—when all the fuel and metal shall be exhausted, but to postpone the inevitable readjustment to a level of increasing cost by the elimination of waste and the improvement of mineral technology.

In any economy, the practice of living out of principal is a dangerous one. In the case of our mineral resources it is unavoidable, since with minerals there is only principal—no income. Doubly dangerous, therefore, is the accelerated use of this wealth, and the more deplorable its waste. With depletion or exhaustion within the scope of possibility, the principal must be guarded with zealous care and foresight.

There was a time, not so long ago, when iron, copper, lead, zinc, gold, and silver were classed as important, and all other metals as subordinate. Advances in technology, metallurgy, and chemistry have largely upset that classification. Nickel, tin, and aluminum, previously considered subordinate, not to mention antimony, chromite, or mercury, have definitely moved into the important class.

Indeed, it would be next to impossible, in this shifting scene of new uses and applications, to say which mineral is important and which is subordinate. Take the case of aluminum as an example. Fifty-seven years ago in the United States the total production for that year was eighty-three pounds. Through the discovery of the process of electrolysis, commercial production was made possible until, by the end of 1908, its total had reached 11,682,779 pounds, and in 1940 amounted to 412,560,000. Today we all know how indispensable aluminum has become both to our national welfare and national economy.

And uranium—vital in atom-smashing, with all its vast potentialities for good and evil: unlocking the incredible reservoirs of power within the atom, making possible an incalculable abundance; transmuting one element into another, as the ancient alchemists dreamed; creating substitutes for all natural products; furthering scientific progress in medicine and other fields of research to a point approaching sheer magic—who knows from what pinnacle of the mineral world uranium, once considered subordinate, may some day look down! Like radium and polonium it is found in pitchblende. Until recently U. 238 was the last and heaviest element known (U being the symbol for uranium, and 238 its atomic weight). As an element it has isotopes which are identical in chemical activity but vary in atomic weight. One of these is U. 235. Physicists who deal with matter and energy and their interrelation, especially in the realm of nuclear physics, were expectantly looking forward to the day when some one would be successful in separating these isotopes and thus find an affirmative answer to the question: Can man release and control the use of atomic energy? That day might be dawning, for according to John J. O'Neill, science editor of New York *Herald-Tribune*, "out of the laboratory has come the announcement that there has been isolated a new strange substance of fantastic properties which can release tremendously vast quantities of atomic energy by a very simple self-sustaining process. . . . The experiment that marked the climax of twenty-five years of effort by scientists all over the world, to smash their way into the nucleus of the atom and release the tremendous stores of energy located there, had been performed." To this the author cautiously adds a statement of his own, "Until however, certain very real problems are solved, atomic power must remain a scientific laboratory accomplishment," and leaves it to the engineers to grapple with the problem of practical application and to make some more observations on "the innate perversity of inanimate matter."

However, between the possibility and the practical commercial fact lies a world of laboratory research and, perhaps, much time. In the meanwhile, we may speculate on the import, if not the impact, this new evolution of applied energy will have. Without any intent to sermonize, there should be an admission of our failure so far to have distributed more evenly the blessings derived from the wider use of mechanical energy. If some day atomic power should become a workaday practical actuality, power magnates would be relieved of the further conscientious scruples which may have motivated their actions in the past. Power would be so universal and so cheap that no one could possibly have any scruples about its adequately distributed use. It would not need to be distributed from central stations or over wires. That, at least, is the story told by those enthusiasts who dramatize and overdramatize what is undoubtedly a scientific achievement of highest social significance.

So, whether important or subordinate in the classifications of today, all our mineral resources must receive more thoughtful attention, not only in the processes of mining and metallurgy, but in their use and preservation.

Extravagant waste of our mineral resources, as of all our other resources, was, and in many instances unfortunately still is, the order of the day. But—whereas the ravages in our forests through ruthless cutting or fire eventually loomed up as an object lesson; whereas drought, dust storms, floods, and the consequences of polluted lakes and streams told their own story—the parallel waste in mining was not so easily apprehended. People did not know that there was a time when, for every ton of coal mined, at least an additional ton was wasted underground.

Illuminating is the fragment of a United States Coal Commission report, in which George S. Rice and J. W. Paul make this statement:

> In western Europe, the average loss of coal in the mining of the beds now worked is from five per cent to ten per cent. In the United States, according to careful field studies in 1923 by engineers of the Bureau of Mines and the United States Coal Commission, the average loss is thirty-five per cent. Of this loss fifteen per cent was considered unavoidable, and twenty per cent avoidable, using the standards of engineering already shown to be feasible by the practice of the better companies. This meant that the avoidable loss amounted to 150,000,000 tons a year, left behind under conditions that virtually prevent its being recovered.

This type of waste increased during the long years of depression, for instead of recovering eighty-five per cent or more, a good many mines in the Appalachian territory showed figures of not more than sixty per cent or sixty-five per cent. A large quantity of coal will therefore be lost for good because the owners could not afford to mine it thoroughly.

Conditions in the non-ferrous metals—copper, lead, and zinc—are likewise unsatisfactory from any angle of use, conservation or otherwise.

Such practices belong to the laissez-faire economy of a bygone age, and since we are as a nation the largest consumer in minerals, and since our per capita needs of metal and fuels far exceed those of any other nation, it will be necessary to make way for more orderly methods of production and use. The National Resources Planning Board has warned us that consumption has increased to such a point that in the last thirty years we have used more oil and coal, iron and copper than in our entire previous history, and the future of our industries depends upon an abundance of cheap metal and cheap fuel.

All over the country there are observable danger signs that the period of cheap metals and fuels is drawing to an end.

In the anthracite fields of Pennsylvania, reported as "only" twenty-nine per cent exhausted, the richest veins are already gone and mining costs are mounting. The same situation prevails in the bituminous fields.

The matchless Mesabi iron-ore range in Minnesota, opened in 1892, is already half exhausted. Its life may last only another forty years. Fortunately, there are available huge tonnages of low-grade ore, but the extraction of this will sharply increase the cost of production.

To pass these warnings blithely by is the most baneful self-deception.

On the bright side of the picture is the fact that engineers and scientists have improved the production of oil and the protection of underground reservoirs against the infiltration of salt water, and have succeeded in deeper drilling—from 3,000 to 10,000 feet. The so-called cracking process has doubled and tripled the percentage of gasoline obtainable from crude oil. Engineers have reduced the average consumption of coal from 5.3 pounds per kilowatt hour in 1908 to 1.5 pounds in 1933, and now, they claim, to less than one pound.

These technological advancements have partly provided

against physical waste. Above all, they have demonstrated the wisdom of conservation, for a barrel of oil today will generate four times as many horse-power-hours of work as it did thirty years ago. But engineers and scientists alone cannot solve the problem unless a way is found for controlling competitive waste through a better organization of the industry.

Take the item of natural gas. There seems to be utter indifference in reference to its waste, and the false impression remains that this waste is a thing of the past. Older citizens remember the great open flambeaus, burning unrestrained night and day, as a visible sign of great natural wealth. Van Hise, in his day, used as an illustration the Caddo field of Louisiana where "seventy million cubic feet per day of gas were wasted, burning without doing any good in any way to anybody." This amount, he said, is equivalent to the daily waste of ten thousand barrels of petroleum. But, as we are now using much more of this resource than we did then, it was found by the National Resources Planning Board that in one field of the United States "a billion cubic feet of natural gas is being blown into the air daily. That, being the equivalent to forty thousand tons of coal, is gas enough to supply the United Kingdom twice over. It is forty times as much gas as all the Scandinavian countries use together. It is almost enough to supply regularly every householder in the United States now consuming either natural or manufactured gas. The only use made of this particular gas is to strip it for the tiny fraction of gasoline which it contains. . . ."

The yearly waste in the Texas panhandle, the committee added, is sufficient to supply all domestic consumers in the state of Texas for a period of seventeen years. It is nearly enough to supply every householder, every store, hotel, and office in the United States, now using natural gas, for a period of twelve months.

In the conservation of our mineral stocks, not only use but re-use is of far-reaching consequence. Fuel resources, as we know, once extracted and expended, are gone for all time. Not so the metallic ones. These are changed from ore to metal, and in that form become working capital. Included in this capital are the scrap piles as well as the manufactured goods.

The secondary metals industry, indeed, dates back to that avid collector of discarded scrap, the junk man. Today he has become a person of prominence, for these junk piles take on ominous significance in cases where a country depends upon foreign sources for its metal.

An interesting example of re-use was given in the National Resources Planning Board report of 1934. Copper, it said, is a relatively industructible metal, which appears and reappears for use many times over. Over the period 1910-1914, according to the report, secondary copper and lead were each equal to fourteen per cent of mine production; by 1924-1928, the proportions had increased to thirty-eight per cent and forty per cent respectively; again, in 1929, to forty-one per cent and forty-eight per cent respectively. In 1933, the tonnage of secondary copper reached the astonishing figure of one hundred and thirty-three per cent of the mine output. Closely following was the recovery of secondary lead, equivalent to eighty-two per cent of the virgin mine metal.

The origin of our huge national scrap pile is little realized. Take lead, for instance. The present great source of lead for re-use is in the storage batteries of old automobiles. When they were first installed about 1911, the annual automobile output was but 210,000 cars and trucks. Today an astounding percentage of discarded batteries—estimated as high as eighty-five per cent—find their way back to the smelter for reprocessing, and thus for re-use.

We are an easy-going people, for the United States is the only important industrial nation that thus far has had no peace-time regulatory measures controlling the exportation of scrap, although this exportation has a large bearing on national and international problems. In fact, through our exports, we not only have furnished other countries with a cheap supply of metal for purposes of war, but we have also put them on a basis for favorable competition in the United States market for fabricated products.

Large American shipments of scrap metal abroad supply the purchasers with the needed metals at a low cost. In normal peacetime we sell from the accumulation of scrap, especially those metals in which we are self-sufficient—iron, copper, lead, aluminum, or zinc—because we have piles of it, and because, as large users of the metal, we keep on adding to the existing stores. These scrap shipments occasionally made the headlines and we heard, for example, on good authority that the purchaser, in the case of Japan, made use of the material, turning it into shot and shell to attack us.

According to Louis B. Ward, M.A., Pd.M., the opposition to the sale of American surpluses to the nations of the world does not come from the people, but is fomented by special interests, which must be detected and exposed. Nations excluded from raw-material markets seek first to create these materials; failing in that, they try to find substitutes; lastly, they fight for them to preserve their national existence.

America is not self-sufficing [he said]. Three choices are open to her. First, she must become self-sufficing, which means a new imperialism if she is to continue to use such things as tin, rubber, and silk. Second, she must find substitutes for these things. Third, she must learn to trade with the nations of the world.

The opposition to our exports to certain nations is not predicated upon a hatred of those nations, but rather the reflection here in America of the economic and commercial wars of the old world. For example, on March 11, 1937, ten European nations organized a scrap-buying Cartel. The agent appointed was the British Iron and Steel Federation of London, England. *The Daily Metal Reporter,* in September, 1939, is authority for the information concerning the cartel.

In 1938, the Cartel bought 1,468,000 tons of scrap metal from the United States. This was fifty per cent of all the scrap sold in export. It exceeded the purchase of Japan, namely, 1,381,000 tons.

That the Cartel is operating politically in America is revealed by the studied attacks against Japanese trade in scrap. It is of interest to the Cartel to break the scrap market. If the Cartel can succeed in breaking that market by the elimination of Japanese purchases, Europe will buy its scrap that much cheaper.

The Lead Cartel was formed in the latter part of 1938 at a meeting of the foreign producers held in London on September 6. Out of it came the Lead Producers Association. Membership included producers in Australia, Burma, Yugoslavia, Canada, and the American Smelting & Refining Company, which had other lead-mining interests in Mexico, Australia, and Newfoundland. The announced purpose of the formation of the Cartel was the curtailment of production to meet consumption demands.

For years, there has been a Cartel operating in zinc, namely, the International Zinc Cartel, which collapsed in 1934.

By 1938, excess production appeared throughout the world, prices were ruinously low.

Efforts were made to reconstitute the Cartel. Naturally, neither Germany nor Italy would join, because they could not afford to curtail domestic production in the face of their exclusion from foreign markets.

The United Kingdom had placed an extremely high tariff on zinc to shut off imports.

Yet, in February, 1938, the International Zinc Sheet Cartel was formed to include the United Kingdom, Belgium, the Netherlands, Germany, France, Spain, Hungary, Poland, Yugoslavia, and Czechoslovakia.

The truth is that in all the basic commodities of the world, either cartels have been established among the nations or strong centralized power under the principles of economic domination has entered the political field, influenced, to say the least, by the desires of the world empires to direct production and sale to those empires and away from their commercial rivals.

The subject of scrap, the Committee of Mineral Policy of the National Resources Planning Board maintains, is "the blind spot of the world's mineral economy." No international statistics are available, and only the United States keeps check on secondary metal returns.

It is estimated that this reserve amounts to about four and a half billion tons. Of this, in 1937, the highest export year, four million, or less than one-tenth of one per cent was shipped abroad. In the following year, this export dropped twenty-five per cent, to around three million tons, while the United States, in the production of pig iron, used twenty-one million tons of scrap at home.

What happened to certain of our resources—land, forests, and minerals—as a result of our participation in the First

World War and our planless action of those days, stands out now as a tragic loss of national wealth, as well as a diminution of national security. It must never happen again.

The damage done to our forests through ill-advised cutting amounted at times to "mining." Terrific waste of sound timber in order to reach particularly select material was but one item. No different is the story on mineral use, especially in the case of coal and oil. In the haste of extraction, prudence was cast aside, and as a result whole deposits have been left in a state of ravage, if not ruin.

Lastly, we remember what happened to the land itself when, after the termination of the war, leaving Europe in the throes of famine, a wild scramble and gamble ensued to replace some 50,000,000 acres which were lost to cultivation in Europe, by putting the plow to 40,000,000 acres, for the most part in the western plains.

From the end of the First World War until 1931, there followed an almost uninterrupted drought, and in 1934 came the most spectacular dust storm of our time. For this occurrence conservators are profoundly thankful, for it achieved in one blow what no amount of reasoning and warning had been able to do in the past—namely, it awakened the nation to the fact that upsetting Nature's balance is an economic sin which if not abjured must lead to social derangement and national decay.

We must realize the fact that mineral resources are both exhaustible and irreplaceable. There is need for control of production, particularly for coal and oil, and incidentally for copper, lead, and zinc. Resource waste should be prevented by proper state legislation, and coupled with this should be the prevention of human waste, the insuring of safety and health for the mine workers, one million men and their families.

The First World War taught us the necessity of preparedness in the handling of our mineral resources. The Second World War only intensifies this lesson.

CHAPTER V

STEPS AND MISSTEPS

THERE is a strong feeling that, since minerals are a common heritage, their use and exploitation should be for the benefit of all, and should be removed from unregulated private exploitation.

England, at this time, has begun a policy of nationalizing coal beds, and in our country there is a tendency to extend public control over natural resources, looking toward ultimate public acquisition and administration.

In the abstract, these proposals may possess merit, yet it seems that our American traditions and practices would promise a much happier solution if we were to continue in private ownership, with proper control of practices on the part of the nation or state. In this manner, the federal government and the states can be enormously helpful through much-needed legislation, providing for the health and safety of the miner and clarifying certain provisions in the Anti-Trust Law, which, though well-meaning, are a source of wasteful operation. In the measure in which the difficulties besetting the mining industry are removed or at least alleviated, better methods, better living, and market conditions will be the result.

Mining, like many other enterprises depending upon natural resources, grew without the wholesome restraint of a consistent national policy. It is high time that we address ourselves to the institution of that quality of order which will not only guarantee better international relations, but will, at the same time, establish decent living conditions for the one million miners and their families who are now helpless victims of the vagaries of economic and social drift.

Above all, we must find a way to reduce the gruesome human toll in mine disasters. Statistics indicate that mining has the highest accident rate, both in frequency and severity, of all industrial occupations. The prevention of accidents, in the very nature of this occupation, is more difficult than in any surface industry. Miners and their families lose between $50,000,000 and $100,000,000 in income annually due to preventable accidents and ill health. The bituminous coal industry finds that upwards of ten per cent of the mine cost of coal is due to factors entering into accident occurrence. If known and available improved safety methods were put into general use, the burden of accident expense could probably be reduced to as low as one or two per cent of production cost.

Under the Constitution, enforcement of safety measures is vested with the states, and, generally speaking, these state laws provide minimum safety requirements. Progressive mining companies have gone further and have adopted additional and more effective measures, which speak an eloquent language in the reduction of accidents. The need for accident and health work in the mines is urgent. A consistent and comprehensive national policy, under which the states and their related industries could operate, would offer a solution.

STEPS AND MISSTEPS

The original task of the national conservation movement, under the leadership of President Theodore Roosevelt, was the protection of the public domain against despoiling by private interests, and the prevention of physical waste.

Of these two major objectives, the former has been fairly attained, but the latter has not fared so well. The waste of gas, oil, and coal now going on—directly ascribable to the destructive competition characteristic of these industries— is deserving of the measured use of the word "intolerable," according to the committee of the National Resources Planning Board.

These wastes are not due to lack of engineering knowledge. Rather, they are due to the rule of competition and, in the special case of oil and gas, to the conflict between the legal facts of surface ownership and the natural facts of geology. Conflict is not really the proper word to use. Disparity would be better. If the consequences of this legal presumptuousness—arresting natural forces operating underground by posting due notice aboveground—were not so pregnant with evil issue and howling cost in waste, it would be downright funny.

The Law of Capture is the euphemistic title given to this procedure. Let us see how it operates.

Ordinary minerals underlying surface property remain in place until removed by the owner of the land or by his authority. Oil and gas, on the contrary, being of fluid nature, remain mobile and flow in the direction of lower pressure— a matter with which the law does not concern itself. Therefore, ownership of oil and gas may only be established by their reduction to possession at the surface, viz., the Law of Capture.

53

This fantastic procedure in turn compels an adjoining lessee to drill in self-defense, although the state of the oil market is one of saturation. To drill, in this case, adds to the glut of a low-price market. Not to drill means final abandonment of his share to his neighbor. The whole matter is a conflict between private cupidity and a system of antiquated laws based on a false premise. Both gas and oil, being mobile, disregard surface boundaries. They are set in motion by drilling and the reckless blowing off of natural gas, which, besides its other values, has that of bringing the oil closer to the surface.

Our chronology at the end of the volume recites that, in 1859, oil was found in Pennsylvania at a place which later became Titusville. The discovery replaced candles with "coal oil." That, in a loose manner of speech, was a beginning. As indication of an initial point of time or space, it is about as precisely bounded and as definite as the irreverent appellation, "Near Beer," which, in its day, painfully misjudged distance.

Oil's condensed biography in a *Who's Who* of minerals might read somewhat as follows:

Petroleum was first described by Herodotus and other ancient writers about 450 B.C., who likely heard of it from others. Was used in the making of plaster and coating of walls, rarely burned in lamps. Indian medicine men used it for magic; braves for mixing war paint. White settlers obtained it from them for medicinal purposes and called it Seneca oil. Within the first half of the nineteenth century, Europe extracted small quantities from shale and used it as fuel in lamps. In 1859 Colonel E. L. Drake drilled the first producing well on Oil Creek, Crawford County, Pennsylvania. Candles gave way to petroleum lamps, Abraham Gesner having conveniently discovered kerosene oil seven years prior to that date. Little other use was made of petroleum until the advent of the gasoline engine. Production of petroleum crept up from zero in 1859 to 5,000,000 barrels of 42 gallons each in 1871; it was 50,000,000 barrels in 1890; and then, with the extensive, incoming use of gasoline engines, it skyrocketed until today the United States production alone is around a billion and a quarter barrels a year. This is the equivalent of about 570,000,000 barrels of petroleum motor fuel.

Petroleum, first regarded as a freak of nature, has become a mainstay of our modern civilization on wheels and wings —with apologies for submarines, bombers, and other flies or flyers in our cultural ointment—and the intelligent legal handling of it has become a national necessity.

From 1909, when the first national inventory of our resources was completed at the request of President Roosevelt, to 1934, when another Roosevelt ordered a second appraisement of our national holdings, is exactly twenty-five years. It was a restless time of political, economic, and social changes, a period of wars and revolutions, accompanied by starvation, pestilence, and the insolvency of nations, an epoch not of reconstruction but portending new and unheard-of shapes and patterns coming from a seething crucible.

The dismal picture of misery in Europe, the realization of the lack of food and raw materials abroad, made us conscious of our own great wealth in land and other resources. It impressed on wider circles the necessity of protecting these sources of plenty. Many states created conservation boards and departments, and the Federal government, through its widely scattered bureaus, extended protective service. Conservation was on the march but, by and large, it remained a movement of academic treatment and value. Move it did, however, and its foremost gain was the realization that more knowledge must be obtained to plan for a better order.

The findings of the National Resources Planning Board created by President Roosevelt are of incalculable value. It should be borne in mind constantly that this is not an administrative, but solely a fact-finding, fact-recording, and fact-facing body. Administrative action must be left to intelligent leadership, whose responsibility it will be to create a free-running engine of public service which will operate on the force of sound policy, independent of erratic political control and selfish interference.

In the meantime, the National Resources Planning Board, through the presentation of facts and still more facts, continues to add voluminous proof that present management of our resources is inept and ineffective, and, if continued, will in the long run prove ruinous.

Approaching the problem of a national mineral policy, its committee starts with recognition of these facts: (1) that private industry has successfully developed the minerals of the United States to an extent never before approximated in the world; (2) that the job on the whole has been done efficiently and without greater wastes or mistakes than were more or less inevitable under existing conditions of enforced competition and widely scattered ownership of the resources; (3) that the desire for efficiency and profit has been mainly responsible for the great gains in conservation practice already made, and (4) that the nature and immense diversity of the problems—scientific, technical, economic, and social —have required a variety, elasticity, and boldness of attack scarcely possible under bureaucratic control, even if it be assumed that such control were competent, honest, and not hampered by shifting political currents.

The committee also believes that mineral reserves are vested with a public interest which justifies the extension of public supervision in such specific conditions affecting our mineral industries as are detrimental both to the public and to the industries themselves, and beyond the power of the industries themselves to remedy.

It is unfortunate that Congress will not act with sufficient speed and circumspection to put the entire problem of conservation into one department. An almost endless array of federal bureaus, permanent and emergency, dabble in this problem, but the complex interrelationship of all is apparently not realized. It is not even taken into account in the one subdivision of minerals where, according to the committee, "no individual policy for coal, oil, or gas, for instance, can be worked out or administered without consideration of their interrelations in a highly competitive fuel market. The same is true in the shifts of demand and the substitutions which are taking place in the national market. A similar lack of a unified approach characterizes our activities with regard to minerals in the foreign field. All agencies of the government dealing with foreign trade or with national defense are concerned with the minerals, yet policies hitherto have often been haphazard and even contradictory."

Depletion and the growing handicaps of mining have

added problems that are extremely difficult of solution. The copper mines of Michigan, for instance, have reached a depth of one mile below the surface, and are by far the deepest copper mines in all the world. At such a depth, they are quite unable to compete with low-cost districts here and abroad.

The consideration of our mineral policies cannot be limited to the national field, for our resources are notably deficient in nickel and tin, for instance, and inadequate in supplies of mercury, tungsten, asbestos, ferrite, china clay, graphite, magnesite, and mica—some of which are so necessary in the production of steel.

To encourage development of certain of these minerals, tariffs have been imposed. But tariffs in themselves cannot develop new supplies. New sources are being discovered, however, through direct appropriations for continuous surveys, exploration, and technological experiments.

Formerly the United States was almost entirely dependent upon Europe for potash. Drilling in New Mexico, Utah, and Texas, through Federal assistance, has now assured an adequate domestic supply.

Similar results have been achieved in the case of helium gas. Whereas in 1917 this gas was available in small quantities at $2,500 per cubic foot, recovery processes, as developed by government scientists, now provide helium gas at about one-half cent per cubic foot, in quantities to meet all domestic needs, and to provide a reserve against future demands.

The problem of conservation is not to prepare for the day when the minerals are gone, but to minimize the readjustment to increasing costs which is, inevitably, merely a matter of time. No mere patchwork, but a national policy, is needed.

Conservation policies of a nation-wide character must be instituted to bring order out of prevailing chaos. Notwithstanding the fact that our entire industrial life depends upon this needed order, minerals have remained the stepchild of our national economy.

To tabulate all the administrative authorities in the field of conservation throughout the country would require a small volume; but here are some of the main branches of the Federal government which preside over the conservation of minerals: (1) the United States Geological Survey and Bureau of Mines, the Department of the Interior; (2) for considering foreign aspects, the Economic Division of the State Department, the Export and Import Bank, the Bureau of Foreign and Domestic Commerce in the Commerce Department, the Tariff Commission, and the Raw Materials Committee of the War Department; (3) the Bureau of the Census, for the collecting of mineral statistics, particularly as related to smelting, refining, burning of cement, lime, gypsum, and clay; (4) the former N.R.A., for the administration of mineral codes of field competition except in the case of petroleum, which is administered by the Petroleum Administrative Board of the Department of the Interior.

All of this, of course, is confusion worse confounded.

In conclusion, be it remembered that the value of minerals produced annually in the United States is about fifty per cent of that of agricultural products derived from the soil. Yet the total appropriation for government mineral services is only one-fiftieth of the appropriations given to similar scientific and technological services in agriculture. Nor is that all that is wrong. These appropriations are scattered through many separate or disjointed bureaus, boards, and departments, and necessarily are used for this, that, or the other specific need—frequently causing overlapping and duplication—instead of being expended according to a comprehensive plan of conservation, which covers the entire problem of minerals as a national resource.

The travesty on conservation in this case is no different from that in the other "branches" of our resources. Branches and branchlets they are, boughs, limbs, and shoots, twigs and sprigs, all suspended in midair from political sky hooks. The heavenly dew of Congressional appropriations falls down upon them. All the branches are there; missing only is the supporting trunk, deeply rooted in national soil.

2. WATER

CHAPTER VI

FLY-OFF, CUT-OFF, AND RUN-OFF

WATER is called the basis of life. Organic tissues, as Van Hise pointed out, are largely composed of water. The average man of 150 pounds, he said, ingests each year about 264 gallons of water or 35 cubic feet, the weight of which is more than a ton. It requires from 10 to 20 tons of water to produce a single bushel of corn, 576 tons to produce a ton of dry clover. And a pound of beef requires directly, and indirectly through the feed, 15 to 30 tons of water.

No single element affects the industrial, commercial, and agricultural development of a country more than its water supply, and no resource in our country has been more wantonly abused.

Water, in reality a mineral, differs from other minerals in that its supply is constantly renewed. What becomes of the enormous quantity of water falling on these United States— a quantity estimated to be equivalent to ten Mississippi rivers?

Science has given us an insight into the complex and diverse phenomena of water's motion, action, and metamorphosis from vapor to liquid or solid and back again. We know that stellar radiation, considered as heat and light, vaporizes sea water and lets the winds carry the load inland where lower temperatures precipitate these vapors in the form of rain, hail, dew, or snow, and immediately the return voyage to the sea is begun via the rivers.

In his *Water as a Resource*, W. G. McGee ingeniously divides this precipitation into three functional classes: the *fly-off*, the *cut-off*, and the *run-off*.

The fly-off is the half of the falling water which evaporates. The cut-off is the one-sixth which is consumed by the plants or which sinks below the surface to join the underground water. The run-off is the remaining third, which follows rivulets, creeks, and rivers back into the sea.

Passing into the atmosphere, the fifty per cent of fly-off repeats the cycle, resulting in further precipitation, which again divides itself into fly-off, cut-off, and run-off. Without this concurrent action by water on land, the amount of water from the ocean could not contribute enough humidity to the air to produce abundant precipitation.

The cut-off moistens the foliage of natural as well as agricultural vegetation; sinking below the ground, it dissolves the earth's salts; reaching the root system, it makes possible plant circulation. A great amount of water is absorbed by the roots and sent upwards through stems and trunks, where it reaches the leaves and through them transpires into the atmosphere.

The balance of the water not absorbed in this fashion sinks deeper to join the underground reservoir. The level at which we find this great but much abused treasure is called the water table. In some sections of the country we still find it a hundred feet or less below the surface, while in others it may be as low as a thousand feet.

Although this underground water is the source of all the springs and wells which serve perhaps fifty to seventy-five

Precipitation and the Hydrologic Cycle

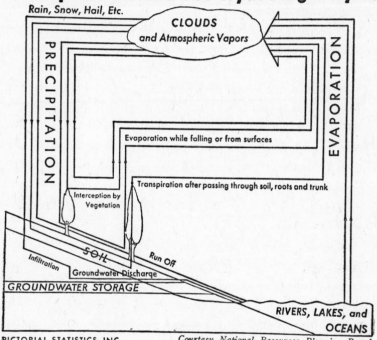

Rain, Snow, Hail, Etc.

CLOUDS
and Atmospheric Vapors

PRECIPITATION

EVAPORATION

Evaporation while falling or from surfaces

Transpiration after passing through soil, roots and trunk

Interception by
Vegetation

SOIL

Run Off

Infiltration

Groundwater Discharge

GROUNDWATER STORAGE

RIVERS, LAKES, and
OCEANS

PICTORIAL STATISTICS, INC.   *Courtesy National Resources Planning Board*

"A drop of water, evaporated from the ocean, rains five times."—Anonymous

per cent of the country's population, not only for their domestic needs but increasingly for irrigation, it is wasted in profligate fashion. This abuse has seriously lowered the water table to such an extent that danger signals are flaring up. Wells are going dry, causing serious loss to industry and agriculture, and no end of annoyance and increase in costs to the people at large.

It has been estimated that careless farming and wanton deforestration have lowered the water table in the eastern states by from ten to forty feet. Three-quarters of the shallow wells and springs have failed.

When it is remembered that this condition did not reveal itself until after long years of abuse, and that it is going from bad to worse, it will readily be seen that protective action is in order. The so-called zone of fracture of the earth in which the underground water is stored is no respecter of state lines. For that reason, interstate and even Federal co-operation may be needed.

Immense as the underground storage is, representing the total precipitation of perhaps half a century, it is by no means unfailing, and may, if lowered still further, become practically unworkable. The waste of underground water has been likened to that of natural gas, because in both cases we are drawing on the stores of the past. Fortunately, in the case of water, we are dealing with a renewable resource, if such renewal is no longer wasted. From the standpoint of conservation, we must realize the utter foolishness, if not wickedness, of squandering the principal instead of living off the surplus accumulation of a self-renewing natural resource. Considering the finely balanced and highly natural functions

66

of its circulation, we must feel the force of impelling duty to help restore the disturbed equilibrium.

The third division of water, that part which goes into the rivers and thence to the ocean, constitutes, as we have said, one-third of the entire amount of precipitation. This becomes available for water supply, for navigation, for irrigation, for water power, for recreation, and, at all times, for sewage disposal, by far the greater quantity of which is untreated raw sewage.

It is fair to assume that the streams may be used for reasonably clean drainage of all kinds. They are the natural drains of the country. But it is unreasonable to admit that they shall be appropriated as the sewer of a few individuals or some cities to the exclusion of the rights of others.

What is the cost of stream pollution—and who pays the bill? A popular conception is that the principal effect of gross stream pollution is the loss of a few fish, which may have served as food or sport for a few individuals. But the report of the National Resources Planning Board throws a different light on the subject. Its first sentence is a classic:

The Ohio River is a sewer, a source of water supply, an outlet for floods, and a highway. One-seventh of the population of the United States is concerned directly with the waters of the Ohio Basin, which present grave dangers and great opportunities.

The Ohio River system now furnishes the chief means of disposal for nearly all the waste products of the many communities that line its banks, and provides the water essential to the health of millions of people and to the operation of thousands of industrial plants. Pollution of the main river and some of its tributaries by untreated domestic sewage and industrial wastes is a constant and serious threat to public health. Acid drainage from mines complicates the problem. It is estimated that the sewage produced by 6,500,000 people drains to the Ohio River directly or through tributaries. Less than thirty per cent of the sewage receives any treatment. On days of minimum flow, about one quart in every gallon of water in the main river at certain points has passed through a sewer system. This grossly polluted water, after filtration, is used as a drinking water by 2,500,000 people.

This is an insufferable situation and what has been said of the Ohio River proper also pertains to the majority of its tributaries. In fact, it holds good throughout the country. Its relative position, however, looms up when we remember that, of the entire run-off in the United States, one-third reaches the sea by way of the Mississippi River. Of this total amount, two-thirds is supplied by the Ohio River.

It has long since become unlawful to use the public highways as a depository of garbage and filth, for it is unsanitary, crude, and wasteful. Modern civilization does not permit it. Yet we continue to use the streams and waterways as a run-off of sewage and manufacturing offal to the detriment of public health and with a consequent loss of much valuable material.

The fight against stream pollution is not a mere matter of sentiment, or an attempt to return the waters to their virgin purity, but rather an effort to prevent manufacturers and municipalities from interfering with the rights of others.

A steel mill, a paper mill, or a starch factory cannot be operated without an immense supply of water being available. Many other industries require an abundance of water for their economic operation, and there are many instances of plants compelled to seek a new location either because the water supply was inadequate or because it had been rendered unfit for use in the industry by waste discharged into it at some point above. It is difficult to estimate the number of industrial plants which have turned away from an otherwise desirable location because the supply of water has been rendered unfit by the wastes of an upstream city or industrial plant.

The damage to farmers and stockmen also is enormous, not only through the loss of animals which drink from sewage-poisoned streams, but from the financial investment necessary to provide wholesome water for farm animals.

Unless an unusual effort is put forward by the people, we are in danger of permitting our rivers to be usurped for one purpose, which, if continued uncontrolled, will exclude their use for practically all other purposes except water power and navigation. If pollution of streams continues unchecked and unregulated, our water courses will be open sewers— unsanitary, foul-smelling, and dangerous to public health; uninviting to lovers of outdoor life, and ruinous to land values.

A practice of this nature is unsound socially as well as economically. Not only are the raw materials of our land wasted, but in our effort to maintain some of the natural charm of our rivers—the fish life—we frequently spend ten dollars in propagation and distribution of fish from hatcheries, when one dollar spent in the protection of the fish naturally in the stream, through preventing pollution, would bring far greater returns to the sportsmen of the state.

A hatchery can, at best, restock a stream that has been fished out, or make plantings in public or private ponds. To attempt to keep a stream stocked with game fish, where fish are killed off periodically by trade waste or where natural spawning is prevented by some toxic material discharged from a sewer, would be a gross misuse of funds.

All the waters of a given state are not seriously polluted. Many still afford most excellent fishing, and the man who is an enthusiast can usually find a reward for his efforts. Serious damage from pollution has, however, occurred in entirely too many streams. Cities and towns, even when sewered, with but a few exceptions discharge their raw wastes, unpurified, into the water courses.

Our factories, which chiefly utilize some agricultural material for the production of a refined food product for the market, discard much material for which so far no profitable utilization has been found. Our canning factories, our large milk condensories, our paper and steel mills each summer season, when the stream flow is low, destroy much, and in many cases all, of the fish life in the water courses for miles below the sewer outfall. Nature strives during the remainder of the year, when conditions for natural propagation, distribution, and growth are more favorable, to correct the damage done, only to see it repeated when an unfavorable situation again occurs.

One of the chief causes of the tremendous waste of raw materials and factory by-products in our industries has been the great abundance of the natural resources of this country and the consequent low cost. As a result, the manufacturer has been inclined to use only what was most profitable and to discard the rest. We must alter this practice if we wish to compete with more thrifty nations.

Probably the treatment of certain industrial wastes, as well as such city wastes—sewage, street cleaning, and ashes —can never be operated at a profit, but this fact does not justify dumping them into the water courses when they injure the public interest.

In many states, conforming with Federal legislation, there has been enacted a law authorizing cities and towns to construct, own, equip, operate, and maintain works for the treatment and the disposal of sewage. It is an enabling act of the most far-reaching beneficial consequences, and it may be set into operation either by the municipalities themselves or by recourse to the Federal Emergency Relief and Construction Act of 1932, Title II, Loans by the Reconstruction Finance Corporation.

Under this title such a project must be self-liquidating, and it is deemed self-liquidating if it is made self-supporting and financially solvent. Such acts fully provide for this by authorizing charges against owners of premises for the use of such works and by providing for the collection of these charges.

This is an economically sound provision. It is in line with existing charges for garbage removal and household offal. Too long we have expected "the other fellow" to pay for such "free" service rendered, each "free" abuse tolerated, not realizing that in the long run we paid for them by taxes and increased costs or losses anyway.

The foregoing has traced mainly the social and economic factors. No reference has been made to the personal loss to many of our citizens, and yet polluted waters have filled thousands of graves in our states with the victims of the diseases carried by this filth. It is a sad commentary on our vaunted progress and development to consider that in the short span of our existence as a nation we have made the great water courses of our land carriers of filth and breeders of disease.

71

CHAPTER VII

INTEREST VS. LAW

CURIOUSLY enough, not only the great conservation movement of 1908 was water-born, as a result of the Inland Waterways Commission appointed to study the use and abuse of our water resource, but our Constitution itself had its inception in a water controversy.

After the northern part of Virginia had been separated from the rest of the colony and given as a proprietory colony to Lord Baltimore in 1632, a peculiar situation arose. Lord Baltimore's gift included control of the Potomac River, so what afterwards became Maryland was in a position to prevent any cargo from landing at any Virginia port along the river. Fortunately for Virgina, an effective check lay in the fact that Cape Charles and Cape Henry controlled the mouth of Chesapeake Bay, and no Maryland vessel could ascend the Potomac if Virginia wanted it stopped.

To James Madison, the most urgent question at this time was that of the navigation of the Potomac. In March, 1785, a meeting of representatives of Virginia and Maryland was called at Alexandria to compose the difficulties. The *deus ex machina* proved to be Washington who, though not a member of the convention, invited the members to Mount Vernon, where, after a four-day session, the treaty between the two contesting states, now known as the Mount Vernon "compact," was drawn up.

This action in the minds of many was in direct violation of the Articles of Confederation, which, like the later Constitution, forbade all compacts between states, and specified that such agreements must receive the consent of Congress. (In an opinion delivered in 1894 in the case of Wharton *vs.* Wise, Chief Justice Fuller clothed this old agreement with the vestments of constitutionality by stating that the agreement was not a "compact" as the term is used in the prohibitions of the Constitution.)

Lest the working agreement might some day prove unworkable, and to settle the question once and for all, the historically famous Annapolis Convention of 1786 was called. Although its members failed to straighten out the matter of interstate trade measures the use of related water courses, and the fixing of uniform tariffs and currency, Alexander Hamilton wrote this convention large on the pages of history when he supported a motion to adjourn and to reconvene later in Philadelphia. At this later meeting, which became the Constitutional Convention, the original Potomac plan became the handy vehicle for the consummation of the national Constitution.

Burton J. Hendrick in his *Bulwark of the Republic* reminds us that, before the Annapolis Convention approach on the part of Maryland and Virginia, Washington had made his trip to the western country and had laid out his transportation route from Virginia to the Ohio.

In this connection, it will be recalled, he had discovered that his plan, because his river system entered Pennsylvania, was an interstate matter. It seemed indispensable that Pennsylvania be invited to co-operate, and, in fact, an invitation for such co-operation had been sent and accepted. . . .

This Mount Vernon compact, next to the Constitution itself, is the most historic paper in our constitutional history. . . . [It] contains many of the principles that ultimately formed the basis of the Constitution. . . . Maryland consented to admit Virginia freely to the navigation of the Potomac; that is, she withdrew the threat, always present, of "occluding"—a popular word of the time—the entrance of that river to the sister state and framing restrictive measures after Virginia's vessels had gained access. Virginia, on her part, contracted to let Maryland vessels pass without hindrance —that is, without the payment of duties—the capes of the Chesapeake and to enjoy all the navigation rights of these waters. A great page in constitutional history unfolds as one reads this interstate agreement of 1785. We foresee New York, several years after the Constitution was adopted, attempting to close its rivers and sounds to the steamboats of its neighbors; we glimpse the coming Daniel Webster proclaiming before the Supreme Court, presided over by John Marshall, the rights under the "commerce clause" of all states to have free entry into the waters of its associates, and Marshall's decision, Gibbons *vs.* Ogden, which sustained that right. It was a decision, says Beveridge, that "has done more to knit the American people into an indivisible nation than any one force in history except only war"; and this principle, expressed so indefinitely in the Constitution that a great legal battle was required forty years after its adoption to reduce it to permanent form, was set forth explicitly in this Mount Vernon compact of 1785.

The need for access to water has been and always will be of paramount importance in the life and rule of man.

Much is being written and spoken on the proper utilization of our water courses, and, as usual, each specialist concerns himself only with his own interests. The water-power engineer sees a stream as stored-up energy, which he seeks to capture and convert into electrical power for lighting our cities and operating their mills. Municipal officials and manufacturers regard it as an outlet for sewers discharging wastes. The sanitarian feels that all streams should be undefiled by any waste, that the problem of purification of water supply may be reduced to a minimum, and that water courses shall not become a factor in spreading disease. The sportsman and the commercial fisherman wish them to be maintained as public harvest fields for their pleasure or financial profit.

Obviously all of these diverse uses cannot prevail. How then shall the water courses be utilized?

Since the inherent conflict of interest in water increases year by year—and with it the multiplicity of our laws—let us look for a moment at the historic progression of this interest.

From the very beginning, water courses have had a vital effect on the growth of the country. In its early history, they served as highways leading into the interior and as a valuable source of food supply.

In later years, their importance has grown as they have provided water and power for our increasing number of industries. But at the same time they have become liabilities as well as assets. Problems of water supply, flood damage, low water, sewage disposal, stream pollution, stream crossings for railroads and highways, and the like, have become more pressing, as the National Resources Planning Board has warned:

Cities have built aqueducts for hundreds of miles to reach watersheds that could be protected from contamination, and they get their electric current in many cases from waterfalls at similar distances. Towns, mines, and factories that used to dispose of their wastes by dumping them into river courses, have been attacked by downstream dwellers for damaging their habitats, threatening their health, and poisoning fish. Rival claimants to water for irrigation projects have brought their conflicting interests before the courts in hundreds of cases. Federal bureaus have been set up to care for both irrigation and drainage projects. Hydro-electric power presents another tangled problem which interests all citizens, from the domestic consumer of electricity to the coal miner, the owner of public utility bonds, the industrialist looking for cheap energy, and the advocate of subsistence homesteads. Rivers that used to be great carriers of goods have become obstacles to the land roads of today— obstacles that must be spanned by bridges costing millions of dollars.

It is a far cry from the town pump of New Amsterdam to the Croton reservoir system a hundred and twenty-miles away. A far cry, too, from the laws and regulations needed to govern a population of some 3,000,000 in 1776, to those needed to serve the present 131,669,275.

Yearly our law-making bodies add prodigiously to the existing numbers of laws, with resulting confusion. Perhaps in no other field of jurisprudence is this confusion so marked as in the case of our water laws.

As long as lawmakers were engaged in adding to the patchwork, frequently in opposition to the existing fabric, the law courts were overwhelmed with demands for interpretations and adjudications. That, after all, is the business of lawyers. But the situation became different when executives were called upon to carry out the laws.

We received our legal form from England, and today we are facing peculiar problems in trying to solve the practical and legal questions arising from conditions affecting riparian rights in Virginia.

When Virginia was settled, three hundred years ago, the Colonists acquired land from the British Crown. These land grants varied with each ruler and none of them were specific in regard to the rights involved.

Ownership of the land, however, did carry with it riparian rights which were not clearly defined.

As the land became more thickly settled, problems arose involving conflicting rights. How was land to be fenced if its boundaries were not defined? Were fish and game public property or did they belong to individual landowners? Who controlled the use of the water for mills and for highways? No one seemed to know.

To add to the confusion, the English doctrine of riparian rights, which maintains that a landowner upstream may enjoy the use of the water so long as he does not interfere by such use with the requirements of his neighbor downstream, failed to survive after it struck the arid regions of the West.

Here the Spanish law prevailed. This was based on the principle that in dry countries, where water is needed for irrigation, and where, owing to scarcity of water, the use becomes limited, only those should be entitled to it who first put a stream to use. In other words, whoever first files on water for a definite beneficial purpose and uses it for that purpose has the first right to it, and no one may later go above him and divert that water in such a way as to make the property of the prior appropriator valueless. Of course, such use must be continuous, or reasonably so.

In order to keep these two basic principles of control over water use at all workable, constant changes and compromises have had to be made in them. We can no longer, it seems to me, in the public interest, consider either water or land wholly as private property. No individual should waste a natural resource or use it harmfully. For instance, he is not entitled to burn forests, even if they are his own property, or to impoverish land by the washing away of the fertile top-soil, or permit his streams to add flood hazards, for these are acts prejudicial to the public interest.

It becomes obvious, therefore, that the water supply of the United States, which affects the welfare of all its people, must be under national control.

All of this had already been perceived in the academic days of conservation following the White House meeting in 1908. In that period of study, of assembling and comparing the material, of assaying its component parts and thus charting the course of its enterprise, the country, so to speak, went to school. A rather advanced school it was, holding to tenets which must have appeared radical, especially to those who, for a long time, had the extended usufruct of the public estate, not only enjoying the fruits, but using up the substance.

A demand was voiced that public property should be returned to public control. This broad statement of principles was made in 1909 by the North American Conservation Conference held in Washington, attended not only by the members of the national commission appointed by the President, but also by commissioners sent by the Governors of Canada and Newfoundland and by the President of Mexico.

The statement on water read in part as follows:

We recognize the waters as a primary resource, and we regard their use for domestic and municipal supply, irrigation, navigation, and power, as interrelated public uses, and properly subject to public control. We therefore favor the complete and concurrent development of the streams and their sources for every useful purpose to which they may be put.

The highest and most necessary use of water is for domestic and municipal purposes. We therefore favor the recognition of this principle in legislation and, where necessary, the subordination of other uses of water thereto. . . .

We regard the monopoly of waters, and especially the monopoly of water power, as peculiarly threatening. No rights to the use of water powers in streams should hereafter be granted in perpetuity. Each grant should be conditioned upon prompt development, continued beneficial use, and the payment of proper compensation to the public for the rights enjoyed; and should be for a definite period only. Such periods should be no longer than [what] is required for reasonable safety of investment. The public authority should retain the right to readjust at stated periods the compensation to the public and to regulate the rates charged, to the end that undue profit or extortion may be prevented.

Where the construction of works to utilize water has been authorized by public authority, and such utilization is necessary for the public welfare, provision should be made for the expropriation of any privately owned land and water rights required for such construction.

If and when these principles of conservation do become law, there is no doubt but that this law will be upheld by the courts. Precedent is given in the following United States Supreme Court rulings:

It is recognized that the state as a quasi sovereign and representative of the interests of the public has a standing in court to protect the atmosphere, the water, and the forests within its territory, irrespective of the assent or dissent of the private owners of the land most immediately concerned. . . . We are of the opinion further that the constitutional power of the state to insist that its natural advantages shall remain unimpaired by its citizens is not dependent upon any nice estimate of the extent of present use or speculation as to future needs.

Rights of property [said Mr. Justice Shaw in another ruling], like all other social and conventional rights, are subject to such reasonable limitation in that enjoyment as shall prevent them from being injurious, and to such reasonable restraints and regulations established by law as the legislature, under the governing and controlling power vested in it by the constitution, may think necessary and expedient.

CHAPTER VIII

ABOLISHING LOCAL PATCHWORK

THE pioneers frequently had to destroy in self-defense. Those who came after them appropriated and exploited the common treasure trove. Let it be said by a grateful posterity that we, the modern pioneers, have come to build and to protect.

In this patriotic labor we have made encouraging headway since 1908. It was easy enough to persuade those who were acquainted with conditions. In fact, they volunteered in great numbers to help conservation authorities and the cause they represented. The difficult part was, and still is, to make plain to the average man that he himself needs protection, just as the resources do; that it is his own house which is afire, not merely his neighbor's.

In a self-governing country we must incessantly seek to obtain wider popular understanding. Public indolence leaves the barn unlocked for thieves to enter and rob. It is, in fact, almost an invitation.

No one can deny that we have made extraordinary strides, yet public education alone is not enough. Enlightened opinion results from a minority, but, when this obtains, the ground is prepared for public action on the part of leaders and statesmen. This is the gradual transition from the static to the dynamic, from the academic to the functional, realm.

81

We are approaching this stage at the present time. There is before us a detailed report of the National Resources Planning Board on a national works plan and program with reference to water. This report should be of particular interest to the citizen and taxpayer because it conclusively shows the need of comprehensive water plans in its working method to divide the country into seventeen drainage basins.

The time-honored belief in local patchwork has been badly shattered. Yet our memories are short. The terrible flood of the Ohio in January, 1937, is all but forgotten, save by the scientist, the engineer, and the National Resources Planning Board.

Floods constitute a horrible waste but, in our present state of progress, not a total waste, for with each new flood comes new awareness of the immensity of our conservation problem, of the interlocking roles of our resources, whereby none may successfully be considered or treated without regard for the whole. The damage done by that tragic flood, from Pittsburgh down to Cairo, started at the uncontrolled headwaters in the Alleghenies.

Floods in one season spell droughts in another. Losses multiply. Loss of lives, property, and livelihood; loss of live stock; loss and suffering through epidemics. But perhaps the greatest loss, because irreparable, is that of our rich soil washed into the sea. When it is remembered that perhaps less than an inch of soil is produced in five hundred years, our complacent neglect of this infinitely precious, this indispensable, resource becomes incomprehensible. If we do not put a determined stop to its loss—and soon—we shall have no further use for our industrial centers, or for the thousands of thriving cities large and small, for we shall be traveling the road which China followed, and face bankruptcy in measurable time.

The flood of the Ohio in 1936 caused a loss of $201,500,-000. This was spoken of as the greatest up to date. Then came another year. This time the January flood caused a monetary loss alone of $411,200,000. Local patchwork must accept a heavy share in the responsibility, for all too frequently the relationships between various types of water problems have been ignored in the making of laws, as has the fact that our water courses serve many purposes.

"During the last few years," declared the National Resources Planning Board, "it has become increasingly apparent that such orderless, unintegrated treatment of water problems, however natural and excusable it may have been under pioneer conditions, should no longer be tolerated."

In the last fifty years, according to the Pittsburgh gauge where flood stage is twenty-five feet, there were no less than sixty-one floods with various stages as high as forty-six feet in 1936—a year which holds the record with four destructive flood levels.

Since water, not the soil, is the final determinant of productive capacity, irrigation is progressively rising in the attainment of higher productivity in regions where the annual rainfall is twenty inches or less.

Egypt, of course, is the classic example of applied irrigation. Indeed, its form of civilization rests upon improved methods of irrigation. Early in their magnificent history, the people of the Nile Valley learned how energy may be saved by such means. The seven fat and the seven lean years resulted from water or its lack.

83

Here in our own country, if we leave aside the evidences of ancient irrigation in New Mexico and Arizona, we find the beginning of modern effort in the lands of the Mormons who settled in that part of Mexico which now constitutes the state of Utah. It was an ideal site for irrigation—desert country, gentle slopes extending westward to the Great Salt Lake, life-giving water flowing down from the Wasatch Mountains beyond. Soon the country was changed into a marvelously productive land.

The trend toward integrated control of irrigation began as far back as 1869 when Major J. W. Powell, a one-armed soldier, and the foremost conservator of his time, went down the Canyon of the Colorado by boat. His studies of the country published in his book *Land of the Arid Region,* coupled with his indefatigable zeal for improvement, were largely responsible for the establishment, in 1888, of the Irrigation Division of the United States Geological Survey, which simultaneously gave authority to the Secretary of the Interior "to withdraw from private entry reservoir sites and other areas which in the future would be necessary for irrigation purposes."

We are prone to consider a *fait accompli* in social or economic advance the result of a mass movement, and are apt to discount or even disregard the creative forces set free by a single man's penetrating vision. Such a man was Major Powell.

Today, irrigation is practiced all over the United States, on millions of acres, chiefly in California, Colorado, Idaho, Montana, Utah, and Wyoming. Such irrigated lands, Van Hise points out, have extraordinary value for the following reasons:

1) Arid lands are very rich in mineral plant food.

2) The amount of water required for a given crop can be regulated.

3) In the warmer parts of the United States, two or more crops may be raised in a single year.

4) Since in arid regions water is turned upon the land, erosion is reduced to a minimum. Indeed, an accumulation of soil is observed rather than its reduction.

Step by step, the work begun by Major Powell continued, resulting in the important Reclamation Act of 1902, which provides that money obtained from the sale of western public lands be used for purposes of irrigation. Congress gave the Secretary of the Interior large discretionary powers of disbursement over this reclamation fund. In its day it was considered socialistic, because it was held that the government was about to engage in business.

The construction work needed for irrigation of a great arid territory, such as ditches, dams, and tunnels, necessitated all kinds of business. Workmen and their families had to be provided for. General stores and boardinghouses had to be operated.

Today that which at one time was bitterly resisted has come about in the most logical manner. The Reclamation Act was the driving wedge. It had as an older brother the Cary Act, passed in 1894, which through co-operation between state and nation and even through their co-operation with individuals, provides for reclamation. Under it Colorado, Idaho, Montana, Nevada, Oregon, Utah, Washington, and Wyoming each received one million acres of Federal land for that purpose.

Congress, unwittingly perhaps, set up a sequence of

causes whose inevitable effect was, and increasingly will continue to be, Federal control through business operation and management. This order of things, desirable or not, was not ordained by a centralized Washington government, but came about because the states' own representatives in Congress demanded more and more Federal funds for state development.

It has often been asserted that the United States has no national parliament, that our Congress is a battleground for obtaining state and regional benefits rather than those of a comprehensive national worth. The fact remains that the states asked for and received unprecedented sums of money; not only that, they asked for and accepted comprehensive plans, as well as the labor of scientists, technicians, and armies of workmen.

We are reminded that Secretary Ickes, charged with the execution of the Public Works Administration Act of 1933, was given large authority and funds but no plans for an orderly procedure. He had to make them himself. In doing so, he not only set up the National Planning Board of the Federal Emergency Administration of Public Works, but followed it by calling on the states for cooperation. The Secretary, through this planning board and its successors, the National Resources Planning Board, "has always urged decentralization of planning—returning to the people back home the major responsibility for the suggestion and sponsorship of plans for the best use of the resources of the local area." In this spirit, in the autumn of 1933, he suggested to the governors of the several states the desirability of following the example of New York, Wisconsin, and a few other commonwealths, in the establishment of state planning agencies.

It is but reasonable that the Federal government, having acquired a large financial interest in the states, should see to it that its investment should be on the basis of sound plans for providing general services and public benefit. The emphasis is on integration of plans. Heretofore public works too often have considered only one factor of use, and thus frequently have conflicted with general use. This was particularly true in regard to water.

To face facts is the method to bring about better order in all things, provided the smaller units of government—state, county, and municipal—substitute business capacity for capricious politics in public management. Above all, we must bring one function into harmony with the next, and one governmental agency into harmony with the other. This refers to all alike.

It has been said that there operate, from the Federal government down to the last township, no less than 175,000 separate governmental units. If by way of orderly planning and simple co-ordination we can show better results, consolidation of overlapping and duplicating authorities will be the logical consequence. Disintegration of public service into 175,000 fragments is responsible for much of the waste, the inefficiency, and the high cost of government. In its excrescences, in addition, it almost puts a premium upon corruption. No single unit is self-sufficient. In simpler days it may have appeared so. Today we have come to realize our interdependence—though as yet we have not fully faced what appears to be a new order but, alas, is only the unfolded growth of advancing gradation.

It is imperative that one central authority have charge of the problem. For it is ultimately one of proper land use and the preservation of our inherited natural wealth, to the end that we may remain a happy, a strong, and a solvent nation.

3. FORESTS

CHAPTER IX

FORESTS AND OUR FUTURE

TREES through the ages have played a highly significant role in the life of man. Forests in their abundance
or lack have spelled the difference between prosperity or
poverty for nations.

When populations were small and resources abundant, no
organized efforts were ever put forth to conserve natural
wealth. Profligate waste always characterized such periods.
One needs only to contrast the biblical description of an
abounding Garden of Eden with the condition of southern
Asia today. Physically, the hills were stripped of their forest
cover. The fertile soils were exhausted by agriculture or
washed down into the lowlands, to be buried later by successive deposits of gravel and sterile subsoil. The soil passed
into the rivers, lakes, and the ocean. The water table fell
below the point where plant life could appropriate it from
the soil to sustain growth.

Biologically, the wonderful balance of nature between
plant and animal species was overthrown. Bird life disap-
peared and insect hordes multiplied to devour the dwindling
agricultural crops.

Nations have risen to power or fallen into obscurity upon
the rise and fall of their natural resources. Tripoli is a
classical example. Once it was a land of teeming population,
while today it has been reduced to a few thousand inhabi-

tants who live in huts of mud and secure their fuel from twisted straw or dried dung.

Earlier civilizations had little or no knowledge or machinery to utilize more than the most accessible of resources, forests, and soil fertility. As these waned, the trend of stronger groups was west and north into eastern, central, and northern Europe. The Mongolian races were halted by the mountains, deserts, and tundras west of the great Chinese empire.

During the Middle Ages, the forests of Italy, Austria, Spain, Germany, and England suffered tremendous overcutting. It took several hundred years for the growing populations of Europe to pass from a desperate need of forest protection and forest products, in daily existence, to the awakening of a public policy of forest restoration and maintenance.

It took France decades of time and prodigious effort and expense to reforest the shifting sand dunes along the Gulf of Gascogne and Pas-de-Calais. Years were spent stopping the destructive erosion and torrential floods coming down from the Alps and Pyrenees to devastate the agricultural lowlands. So, while a pioneer people was working prodigally to remove the forest cover of a newly discovered America on one side of the Atlantic, older civilizations in France, Germany, and Austria were striving equally hard to regain the same resources which they, in their youth, had failed to maintain.

The standard of living of any human period or country in the world has always depended upon the natural resources available, plus climate and the ability of human ingenuity to exploit them.

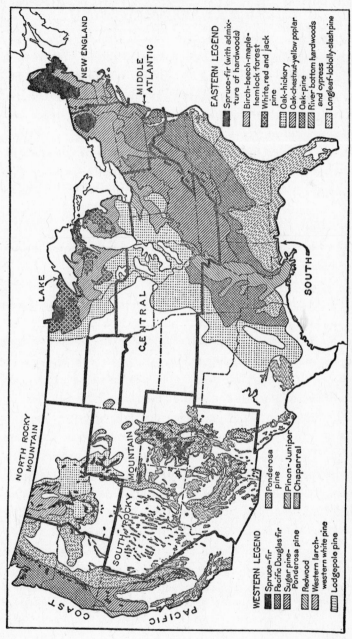

Forest regions and principal types of forest (based on forest cover map "Forests of the United States" by Zon and Shantz).

EASTERN LEGEND

- Spruce–fir (with admixture of hardwoods)
- Birch–beech–maple–hemlock forest
- White, red and jack pine
- Oak–hickory
- Oak–chestnut–yellow poplar
- Oak–pine
- River bottom hardwoods and cypress
- Longleaf–loblolly–slash pine

WESTERN LEGEND

- Spruce–fir
- Pacific Douglas fir
- Sugar pine–Ponderosa pine
- Redwood
- Western larch–western white pine
- Lodgepole pine
- Ponderosa pine
- Pinon–Juniper
- Chaparral

It has been said that the primeval forests in these United States were nowhere on earth exceeded either in extent or value. Because of different conditions of climate, soil, and topography, they varied widely. It has been estimated that the original 822,000,000 acres of our virgin forests contained a total of 810 species of native forest trees, of which 600 species were native to the eastern parts of the country, 227 species to the western parts of the country, and 17 species common to both. A concrete conception of this diversity may be gained by studying map on page 93 which shows both forest regions and the principal types of forests.

The question naturally arises: How have we, as a nation, been using our 822,000,000 acres of forests?

As long as timber was universally available it was natural that it should be used. Fifty years ago in America the frame house was the standard, brick and stone houses the exception. The most popular building undoubtedly was, and in a sense still is, the American log cabin, which, of course, was the most convenient architecture for a people who had a superabundance of perfect timber but no sawmills.

The log cabin, which we generally regard in this country as typically American, seems to have been a Swedish importation. Three hundred years ago a colonizing expedition of Swedes and Finns came to Delaware Bay, where Fort Christina was established. They were familiar with the log cabin, which had been used in Sweden for hundreds of years. Timber being abundant, they built log buildings here.

The English and Dutch colonists were not familiar with the log cabin and built temporary shelters, later replacing them with frame and masonry houses such as they had known in England and Holland. But the Swedish example resulted

94

in widespread log-cabin construction by the end of the seventeenth century.

The forest, too, was the source of one of the first American industries—the manufacture of potash from wood ashes. Hardwoods were generally used for this purpose. Their ashes were first crushed in large wooden containers with holes in the bottom. Water was poured over these until all the "ley" was leached out. After that the liquid was boiled in iron pots and the resulting lye salts removed. Combined with fat, the result was soap. The potash was also used in making "saleratus" for baking purposes—the forerunner of our present-day baking soda.

Charcoal, once produced, was found useful in making gunpowder, and in the reduction of iron ores.

The English navy at an early date discovered the value of New England white pine for masts and spars.

So the forest began supporting the struggling colonies not only with homes, plank roads, and fuel, but with ever-expanding industries. The production of naval stores came next.

England needed an independent source of pitch, tar, and turpentine. Since its dependence upon the Baltic provinces was none too secure in a time of fluctuating fortunes of war, Butler, in his *American Conservation*, reminds us that

one of the reasons given for the settlement of Jamestown was the hope of England to develop a source of pitch, tar, and turpentine. The development of the naval stores industry in the southern colonies languished until near the close of the seventeenth century. In the meantime, a considerable trade in naval stores developed in New England from the Plymouth colony. The production was not large, however, since New England pines were low in the yield of "pitche."

By the close of the seventeenth century, the high yields of the southern pines in pitch, tar, rosin, and turpentine began to be taken advantage of and extraction in New England gradually became negligible. The southern industry was greatly stimulated by encouragement from England. Between 1700 and 1718, for example, shipments of tar alone from the colonies to England jumped from 177 to over 82,000 barrels. From that period on, the Southern States have not only kept their supremacy in naval stores production, but they have maintained a virtual monopoly of it in America, because the southern pine forests are so rich in rosin that no other forest region in the country can successfully compete with them. Through three centuries these southern forests have maintained the naval stores industry, one of the most important in the Southern States, and have given the United States the distinction of leading the world in the production of naval stores.

Today about two-thirds of the world's naval stores are produced in the South.

We still speak of naval stores, although the various products included in this category are now used in the manufacture of all types of commodities. For instance, turpentine and rosin, derived from the long-leaf pine and the slash pine, have a host of uses: in the making of printing inks; as a preventative for bleeding; in the manufacture of woolen print goods; in floor and furniture polishes; in laundry glosses; in washing preparations; in stove polishes; in soaps, both medicated and plain; in the finishing of writing and printing paper; in the manufacture of fireworks, explosives, medicines, disinfectants, and liniments.

Captain I. F. Eldredge, of the Forest Service, a few years ago made a survey of the naval stores situation and prospects, covering an area of approximately 65,000,000 acres, which contained nearly three-fourths productive forest land.

In the naval stores belt as a whole, he found the naval stores timber supply to be adequate, but he warned that this was not necessarily true for each of the survey units into which the belt had been divided. The units surveyed are in South Carolina, Georgia, Alabama, Mississippi, Florida, and Louisiana.

Captain Eldredge warned that a reserve growing stock should be built up in several localities. In the past few years, a number of large pulp mills have been established in the naval stores region, making an additional drain on the available timber.

Partly through the efforts and demonstrations of Dr. Herty, southern pine may now be used successfully for the production of rayon, newsprint paper, and heavy wrapping paper. Through this recent development, the South has joined other parts of the country in building up paper making to the fifth American industry in point of value.

Man has advanced fast and far since the day when he learned the process of paper making from the wasps, who, by chewing fiber, produce wood pulp, out of which they build their nests. Today paper is used and produced in almost unbelievable quantities in this country. Our annual per capita consumption is figured at 226 pounds. Our national annual consumption varies between 12,000,000 and 14,000,000 tons. In all classifications of paper, except newsprint, we produce more than we consume. Of the total world's production of newsprint, we consume twenty-five per cent, but produce only eight per cent. The difference has had to be supplied by foreign countries—notably Canada and Finland. Yet someone has figured that we annually produce enough newsprint to reach to the moon and back seventy-five times.

Science and research tell us that although the forest has furthered our industrial advancement amazingly up to date —giving us homes, fuel, naval stores, paper; helping us duplicate textiles more or less successfully; providing us with more than sixty chemical compounds from wood distillation, from wood charcoal to wood alcohol and wood vinegar—we have really seen nothing yet. More and greater wonders are in the offing.

We have watched the oldtime plank roads disappear, to be replaced by macadam and other modern surfacing substitutes. We have seen gas, gasoline, oil, coal, and electricity supplant wood, which was the initial fuel of the country and still is tremendously popular, but an almost unobtainable luxury outside the farmer's wood lot. But by no stretch of the imagination can we visualize the time foreseen by the chemist, when lumber will no longer be produced by nature in its natural form, but will be developed from pulp, on order, in any size, length, specific gravity, or shape desired. When that time comes, it will spell the salvation of our forests or what happily remains of them.

Chemistry, rising to the needs of forest conservation, seems destined to change the entire forest practices of the world, and change them for the better. Today we still base our estimates on mature and immature timber. Tomorrow that distinction may be wiped out. Any growth large enough for the production of pulp will be able to vie in marketability with naturally produced mature timber.

Floors, walls, ceilings, furniture, and decorative objects

will be increasingly made of plastics. Tough, transparent, moisture-proof cellophane—only in part a product of wood pulp—is replacing paper for many types of wrapping; but new and varied uses for it are coming in great profusion. The fine finish of our modern furniture and automobiles may have a cellulose nitrate base. Cellulose treated with nitric acid is the base of smokeless powder. "New Skin" is practically the same thing. By the addition of camphor this same cellulose nitrate forms celluloid, used in the manufacture of jewelry, combs, brushes, fountain pens, glass frames—and, for the better part of the closing decade of the last century, that cause of much merriment, the celluloid collar.

One cannot condemn the use of our forest products in themselves, for they have gone into homes, transportation, industry, warmth, and even art and beauty. We do stand guilty, however, before present and unborn generations for the destruction of forestry and agriculture upon the lands we have laid waste.

In this country, the lumbering wave swept down from the New England States to New York and Pennsylvania, then northwest through the Lake States, and onward through the Central States and into the great cypress and pine forests of the South. Today the great virgin forests are making their last stand in the Pacific Northwest.

While, often too late, other countries have been aroused to the necessity of rebuilding their forest resources, we in America have blindly and consistently failed to profit from their mistakes. The time has now come when we must!

Without trees, we could not carry on our daily existence. From the cradle to the grave we use wood in endless variety and form: from houses to matches; from railroad ties to rayon garments; from citrous boxes to newspapers; from pyrolignites to turpentine.

Without trees, our hillsides and river slopes would soon become desert land. This has already happened in many places, with the additional evil of flood destruction. When the Ohio River slopes were denuded of trees, the fine rich soil followed. Ask our farmer friends in the Ohio River bottom what is happening now; why each new flood is leaving more broken stone, sand, and gravel, instead of the good rich soil they once received.

Without trees, evaporation of needed moisture and exhalation of oxygen fails. Water formerly held by the thick leaf mold rushes off instead of being distributed gradually through many smaller streams of steady flow. Aquatic life suffers. Fishing streams dry up.

Without trees, no home remains for the big and small game which once upon a time roamed the fastness of our woods.

Without trees, birds have no protection from their natural enemies. And a world without birds would bring about man's abdication in favor of a wild reign of insects. There are but 18,000 species of vertebrates—man included—against more than 350,000 species of insects.

Chemistry can go only so far, by providing us with ways and means to make our depleted forest reserves last longer. Nothing can replace either the inspirational beauty or the functional soil-, water-, bird-, beast-, and even man-preserving properties of our trees—except more trees.

CHAPTER X

TAKING STOCK

WITH the thought ever before us that the decline of a nation has proceeded simultaneously with the destruction of its keystone natural resources—its forests—let us examine our present situation.

Out of our original 822,000,000 acres of forest land, we now have 630,000,000 acres—462,000,000 acres being classed as commercial, 168,000,000 acres as non-commercial. On these the *Forest Lands of the United States* report of the Joint Committee on Forestry brought out the following facts:

One-third of the forest lands are to be found in the South. Sixty per cent are east of the plains region, where four-fifths of the nation's population and industry are located.

While three-fourths of our forest land, or 462,000,000 acres, is still suited to timber growing, nearly 77,000,000 acres—an area double the size of New England—is now practically non-productive; another 71,000,000 bears trees too small for saw timber; about 101,000,000 acres is in trees of cordwood size; about 213,000,000 acres support trees of saw-timber size.

The United States Forest Service estimates that, because of poor quality, inferior species, remoteness, and so forth, not over two-thirds of the saw timber is economically avail-

101

AMERICA'S NATURAL WEALTH

able under present market conditions; that the great bulk
of the young saw timber and the smaller or cordwood-size
material should, of course, be retained as growing stock—
the forest capital from which future sustained yield or forest
"interest" must be derived; that even during recent subnor-
mal years second-growth saw timber is being cut or destroyed about as fast as it is growing, while the volume of
old growth is being steadily reduced.

CURRENT ANNUAL GROWTH AND DRAIN IN THE
UNITED STATES, 1936

Region	Combined saw timber and cordwood (million cubic feet)		Saw timber (million feet, board measure)	
	Growth	Drain	Growth	Drain
Northeastern	1,260	1,370	2,625	2,468
Central	568	907	978	1,781
Lake	979	983	1,850	2,420
South	6,495	6,689	20,403	23,642
Columbia River Basin	1,634	2,849	5,247	14,264
California	155	501	414	2,649
South Rocky Mountain	196	164	516	584
Plains	—	—		
Total	11,287	13,463	32,033	47,808

Forest Service figures show that in 1936 the total drain through
cutting and losses by fire, insects, disease, and so forth, on our combined forest capital of saw timber or cordwood-size material exceeded growth of 2,200,000,000 cubic feet.

The drain on saw timber, estimated at 47,800,000,000 board feet,
exceeded total saw timber growth by 15,800,000,000 board feet or
by fifty per cent. This drain exceeded growth in every major forest
region except the Northeast. Because of poor quality, species, and
remote location, not all growth really counts. Drain exceeded effec-

tive growth by an additional 4,500,000,000 board feet. This relation between saw timber drain and growth is still less favorable because drain averages to be of higher quality material than does growth.

These statements indicate clearly the trend of the drain on our forests. More recent estimates on total lumber requirements point toward a 34,000,000,000 foot cut in 1941, and may reach 38,000,000,000 feet in 1942, according to George S. Trayer, writing in the *Journal of Forestry* for September, 1941, on "Forests and Defense."

With such a prospect in the offing, it is the more alarming that only a part of this titanic lumber pile serves a useful purpose; only a part of it justifies its cutting at all.

The waste of our timber has been and still is monstrous. It has been estimated that through logging operations one-fourth is wasted directly. When the logs go to the mill, losses estimated all the way from thirty to sixty per cent are added. Applying the lowest estimate, thirty per cent, we find forty-seven and one-half per cent of the original stand cut has been wasted before the timber reaches the wood industries. Here a loss of another one-fourth occurs, leaving a residue of a mere thirty-seven and one-half per cent of the original forest yield as the portion which serves its intended purpose.

And this has been going on ever since the holocaust of American lumbering started in the New England States and swept the length and breadth of the country.

As long as we let this condition prevail, all talk of conservation is basically futile. By such wanton and wholesale destruction we are throwing away not only our immediate values, but those of our children. We are permitting the greed and carelessness of the few to change the very condi-

tion and appearance of our land; making it barren; inviting
fire; encouraging the washing away of soil; presaging an inadequate and irregular water flow.

Forest fires are now a deadly scourge the country over,
taking a high toll of life, property, and soil fertility. The
Joint Committee on Forestry reported on a recent forest fire
as follows:

Within a few miles of Portland, Oregon, the committee was
shown the Tillamock burn, an area of about 250,000 acres, formerly
containing 10,250,000,000 board feet of merchantable timber. Fire
destroyed this area in 1933 and burned it over again in 1939. This
timberland is largely owned by private companies, who were cutting
timber at the time the fire broke out. Millions of dollars were lost
in this fire, which probably could have been prevented for a few
cents per acre.

Contrary to public opinion, in such a fire the greatest loss
is not the destruction of mature trees, for a considerable part
of them can still be utilized. The chief loss lies in the devastation of the young growth and the impairment of the forest
floor. Burned-over areas furthermore are subject to recur-
rent conflagration.

Our idea of "putting out a fire," i.e., starting one, seems
to have been inspired by the Indian, who had much practice
with forest fires in his burning of forest and woodland to
produce meadows which the big game would seek. Some authorities believe that much of the existing prairie land was
once woodland, but through Indian practice was changed to
its present form. More specifically, they refer to that pocket
in the Kentucky Appalachians now known as the Blue Grass
Region.

While as yet we haven't succeeded, in the majority of the

states, in bringing about adequate control of fires, the United States Forest Service on the other hand has reduced its fire loss to one-twentieth of one per cent. In this it has had considerable co-operation on the part of some of the timber landowners. In some of our states, particularly in the Northeast, forest-fire control is already well organized, and fire losses are gradually being reduced.

Evidence that destructive exploitation of our timber resources has caused unfavorable economic conditions in many forest regions, particularly Washington and Oregon, is becoming increasingly apparent. The Grays Harbor district, for instance, was built up almost entirely on forest industries. In 1929 it contained thirty-four sawmills and thirty-seven other wood-using plants; by 1939 there were only ten and twenty-one respectively—20,000 parcels of tax-delinquent lands and pay rolls twenty-five per cent of those in 1929. Old-growth Douglas fir was virtually exhausted. This trend of destructive forest liquidation, declared the Joint Committee of Forestry, is particularly serious because the economic structure of these two states is keyed to the lumber industry, which supports sixty-five per cent of the industrial pay roll.

Millions of acres of cut-over land have become tax delinquent and abandoned. This situation is especially serious in the Pacific Northwest, the Lake States, and parts of the South. In Oregon and Washington, for example, the amount of forest land thus forfeited rose from about 1,140,000 acres in 1933 to more than 1,850,000 in 1938. Forest land tax delinquent for at least three years in those two States rose from 3,560,000 to 5,370,000 acres. In December, 1939, one of the Coos County, Oregon, local newspapers carried fifty-two pages advertising tax-delinquent lands. In the three Lake States, tax delinquency on cut-over forest lands rose from 6,000,000 acres in 1929 to more than 20,000,000 in 1939. The Federal Government now owns 32,000,000 acres, or about fifty-two per cent of the land in Oregon.

For every instance of specific abuse of our forest resource, we can put our finger on the cause.

Why must millions of acres of forest land in Minnesota, Wisconsin, Michigan, and Pennsylvania, which once supported heavy stands of timber and were stocked with all sorts of game and other wildlife, now remain partially or entirely non-productive? The answer is human greed and carelessness. Where magnificent trees once grew, forest fires have not only robbed the next generation of a standing wood supply, but have taken away time and again the soil cover and fertility needed to sustain new growth. This condition prevails over vast areas and it will take many long decades before this humus can be rebuilt by successive types of vegetation to the point where the land will again be able to sustain a forest stand.

Why should the small wood lots, so precious to every farm throughout the agricultural states, such as Illinois, Indiana, and Ohio, be neglected and ignored both by the landowner and the agricultural leader as a potential crop and therefore a part of farm management? The answer is lack of vision, which permits grazing animals to eat up the young trees, on the forest floor, that are necessary to perpetuate species and to link one crop of timber with the next. While busily engaged in building up the quality of grain and animal crops through careful selection and breeding and by eliminating the "border" individual, we have been permitting the lumber man to haul away only the best timber, leaving the

106

cull and overmature trees to occupy and perpetuate the site.

Why do the deforested states east of the Great Plains import millions of dollars' worth of lumber and other forest products each year when there are millions of idle and eroding hill acres in each of these states, increasing at an appalling rate? Take, for example, the rough, unglaciated hill lands of southern Ohio, Indiana, and Illinois. Once the cradle of these states, they stand today as a great economic problem in land use.

The early pioneers who came down the Ohio River pushed northward through the hills. It was necessary to settle on high ground because the low flat lands were undrained and unfit for healthy living. So the forests on the hills were cleared away, and the plow turned under the protecting leaves and humus, leaving loose soil exposed to erosion. Fertility was quickly leached out because the lime and nitrates —the basic plant foods—are readily soluble in rain.

Then came dredging machinery to transform lowlands into fertile grain fields. Governmental projects of expansion in agriculture caused the deserts to produce. Each acre of new soil with its virgin fertility placed several acres of older hill land on a marginal producing basis.

In an effort to feed the world during the First World War, agricultural expansion was stimulated far beyond normal requirements. When world markets were curtailed after the war, it was natural for the easily cultivated lands to remain in production while thousands of hill farms could be managed no longer on a profitable basis.

Each abandoned farm in the hills of Kentucky, Tennessee, Ohio, Illinois, Indiana, and Missouri shifted a greater burden upon the ones that remained. Schools, roads, eleemosynary institutions, and public governments began to suffer from a lack of taxable wealth. Mounting taxes due to abandoned farms increased the rate of emigration still further. Township roads could not be maintained because taxes were inadequate. The impassable mud roads aroused new disgust as the hill farmers acquired automobiles. Instead of driving in and out to their hill farms, increasing numbers decided on a last one-way trip—out.

Schools suffered simultaneously with the roads. Consolidation helped the situation temporarily. Eventually the roads became so bad in many places that the pupils could no longer be transported in and out.

So the great American migration from the hills continued. The old fields abandoned to weeds became new preys to erosion. Thousands of tons of the scant remaining soil also left the hills for good, and found their way into the tributaries of the Mississippi, lost for all time to the production of hillside vegetation which might eventually make possible new hillside forests.

The nation would rise in defense of a fractional acre taken from it by a foreign foe. Yet we have stood by and permitted our great forest wealth and its soil to be wasted, robbed of its fertility, burned and plundered by its beneficiaries, and finally neglected so that what little potential productive capacity it has retained is being stripped by the wind and weather.

As guardians of our great forest preserves—only temporarily in possession—we have been, to say the least, myopic. Let us recognize the wisdom of the forester who, taking a long view, seeks to avert the experience of older nations with wasted soils and timber famines. Let us remove thousands of

acres of marginal producing land from agricultural competition and acquire it for forestry—if not for immediate benefits to ourselves and our children, at least for our children's
children, lest we fulfill the prophecy of the sage: "Where
there is no vision, the people perish."

CHAPTER XI

WHITHER NOW?

IT IS a lesson from the history of civilization, a lesson repeated over and over, that every nation in due time reaches the crossroads where it must choose its new direction, its "Whither Now?" One road leads to quick success, to the enjoyment of privileges, to pleasures and irresponsible gratification. It is by far the easier way. The other road points to arduous work, hardship, and endurance, to the willing assumption of public duties and the cheerful discharge of them. It is much the harder way, but in the handling of our forest resource it is the only way, if we as a nation are to survive.

When we consider that forestry in this country is only sixty-eight years old, and when we ponder the magnitude of the task, we realize what a debt we owe to the men and organizations who first sponsored this movement and are at present carrying it forward.

In 1873, at the suggestion of Dr. Franklin H. Hough, the American Association for the Advancement of Science addressed a statement to Congress, as well as to the states, demanding legislation for the protection of forests.

In 1875, Dr. John A. Warder of Ohio, together with a group of Chicago friends, organized the American Forestry Association, in order to promote the principles of forestry.

WHITHER NOW?

In 1876, with authorization by Congress, the Department of Agriculture appointed Dr. Hough as Forestry Agent.

In 1877, Carl Schurz, then Secretary of the Interior, urged the establishment of Federal forest reservations.

Looking back over the achievements of the American Forestry Association, Ovid Butler, its executive secretary, stressed the importance of the Cincinnati meeting of 1882, out of which came a merging of the American Forest Congress with the American Forestry Association, marking the real beginning of the Association's national activities.

In his *American Conservation*, he says of this meeting and its consequences:

The Congress was notable on two accounts. First, it organized public sentiment on a larger and more influential scale than ever before. Second, it brought into the movement Dr. Bernard E. Fernow, a trained forester from Prussia, who had come to America a few years before. Dr. Fernow became the Secretary and spearhead of the Association, serving until selected, in 1886, to head the Division of Forestry in the Department of Agriculture. Under his leadership the Association began a national campaign for forestry, one objective of which was legislation by Congress to reserve timbered portions of the public domain and to place them under forest administration.

In 1891, Congress passed an act giving the President authority to withdraw areas of the public domain as forest reserves. There were, of course, loudly voiced protests that the forest reserves were being locked away from the people. Unfortunately, the Act did not make any provisions for protecting or administering the reserves.

In 1892, President Harrison created the first reserve—the Yellowstone National Park Timberland Reserve—in

Wyoming, and before his term expired he had set aside forest reservations totaling 13,000,000 acres.

In 1896, the Secretary of the Interior, at the request of the American Forestry Association, asked the National Academy of Sciences to draw up a plan for administering the public forest reserves. As a result of its recommendations, President Cleveland, on February 22, 1897, added 20,000,000 acres to the forest reserve system, and on June 4, 1907, Congress passed an Act providing for the administration of the reserves.

These public lands, which had been withdrawn as forest reserves, became the objects of fierce controversy. Western groups which had come to regard all unfenced land as their own domain, fought every step of the government, which was already handicapped in the huge undertaking. The Department of the Interior had no foresters—a situation which did not help in administering forest reserves. The Division of Forestry in the Department of Agriculture contained less than a dozen men.

In 1898, Gifford Pinchot became head of the Division of Forestry. Within seven years, he increased his department from eleven to over eight hundred men and greatly expanded its functions.

In 1901, Theodore Roosevelt, in his first message to Congress, ridiculed the system of having the government's foresters separated from the government's forests. He recommended that the reserves be placed under the Bureau of Forestry. Congress refused.

In December, 1904, Roosevelt repeated his recommendations. A few weeks later there was held in Washington an

WHITHER NOW?

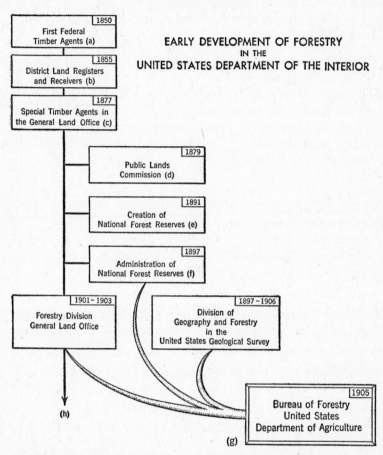

EARLY DEVELOPMENT OF FORESTRY
IN THE
UNITED STATES DEPARTMENT OF THE INTERIOR

(a) Prior to the creation of the federal Department of the Interior in 1849 occasional timber agents were appointed by the Solicitor of the Treasury under the law of 1831.

(b) Special timber agents appointed in 1859 were discontinued. Their duties were added to district land office registers and receivers of the General Land Office.

(c) Carl Schurz, among the foremost advocates of forestry, served as Secretary of the Interior from 1877-1881.

(d) Submitted a 700-page report within a year.

(e) The President was authorized by Congress to set aside national forest reserves out of the public domain by special proclamation.

(f) From 1897 to 1905 administered by the Department of the Interior.

(g) Congress, in 1905, merged practically all federal forestry functions and activities into the Bureau of Forestry of the Department of Agriculture.

(h) Custodianship of land-title records, jurisdiction over mineral resources, and control of Indian forest lands remained in the Department of the Interior.

113

American Forest Congress called by the American Forestry Association.

It was [declared Ovid Butler] the most notable gathering of leaders of science and industry ever to attend a forestry meeting. It dramatized as never before the whole question of the conservation of natural resources. One of its resolutions called upon the Congress of the United States for immediate action in unifying "all the forest work of the Government, including the national forest reserves, in the Department of Agriculture." The meeting, held at a psychological moment and reflecting an aroused sentiment of the nation, is credited with having been a deciding influence upon Congress. In any event, Congress three weeks later passed the Act of February 1, 1905, transferring the forest reserves to the jurisdiction of the Department of Agriculture. On July 1, 1907, the Bureau of Forestry became the Forest Service and the reserves were given the official designation of National Forests.

It has often been asked why the transfer was made at all. To those responsible for it, it was plain that comparatively large sums of money by way of appropriation were needed to carry on the work. It was felt that the Department of Agriculture was in a better position to obtain these appropriations from Congress, for it would have been almost impossible to obtain the same amounts for a Department which, at that time, was directed by law to give away land rather than to acquire it.

At the present time, the question of whether or not the Forest Service should be left in the Department of Agriculture or transferred to another of the existing departments, or to a newly created Conservation Department, is still being discussed.

The number of Federal agencies dealing with forestry and conservation policies and practices has materially in-

creased during the past few decades. A glance at the chart
on page 117 will suggest their complexity.

In addition to all the Federal agencies, forty-two of the
forty-eight states have administrative units in their governmental structure dealing with forestry matters; colleges and
universities maintain forestry departments; and there are at
present one hundred and seventy-five associations and organizations dealing with forestry.

With all this developed interest in forestry, it would seem
as though our remaining forests would be amply protected.
But that is not the case. The absence thus far of a functional
Federal policy results in duplication of effort and in neglected opportunities. Perpetual conflict and irritation between contending government agencies brings dire results,
in sins of omission if not in sins of commission. Private greed
and stupidity have not yet been adequately curtailed.

In the beginning, we fell heir to a magnificent national
domain. Parts of it are irretrievably gone. It is of the utmost
importance that we do not repeat, in our last glorious remnant in the Northwest, the slaughter that we permitted in
all the other timber regions of our country. We as a people
must demand a change of policy which will preclude this.
Otherwise all well-meant attempts to plot, to survey, to "in-
terpret" the situation as it is, will prove meaningless, if, as
heretofore, the ax invariably has the last word.

Militant public opinion would soon be aroused if all could
visit the still marvelously clothed mountains and hills of our
Far West; could walk through the giant sequoia groves of
northern California; could feel the majesty of a great American forest such as those of Douglas fir, Sitka spruce, and

western red cedar in Oregon or Washington, particularly in the Cascade Mountains.

When you stand in these high-vaulted temples of nature and are told that all this glory must fall under the ax because nearby mill-town populations must live, you wonder what these same mill-town populations are going to do a generation hence. If you advance the theory that such forests are surely more valuable, not only to the country as a whole but to the mill towns in particular, than the equivalent amount of cut timber could ever be, you are met by the argument that, after all, the forests are a renewable resource.

Manifestly a renewable resource is one which, through its own inherent forces or assisted by the hand of man, renews itself. Giants of the forest, hundreds and in some cases a thousand years old, may be renewable, and then again they may not be. So much would depend on circumstances during the next thousand years. Under the best of conditions, such renewal will be so long drawn out that the practical value of it will be lost.

When the United States Forest Service speaks of forests as a renewable resource, it is not using *renewable* in the same sense as the lumber interests, who have no compunction whatsoever about cutting down redwood stands from five hundred to a thousand years old, "because, after all, trees are renewable." If this is true, are the lumber interests prepared, so far as their financial setup is concerned, to wait another five hundred to a thousand years to be sure such reproduction takes place and, if not, to compensate for its lack? Of course they are not.

The interest of the people in the state and in the nation at large demands a reorientation on the subject of just how

WHITHER NOW?

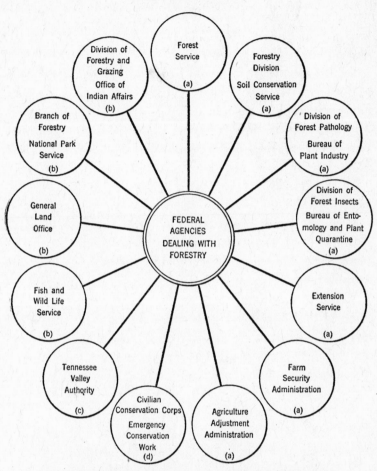

(a) In Department of Agriculture   (c) An Independent Agency
(b) In Department of the Interior   (d) In Federal Security Agency

ADDITIONAL FEDERAL AGENCIES CONCERNED WITH FORESTRY

Bureau of Agricultural Economics in Department of Agriculture.

Bureau of Foreign and Domestic Commerce, the Weather Bureau and the Census Bureau in the Department of Commerce.

The Director of Forests, the Grazing Service and the Division of Territories and Island Possessions in Department of the Interior.

Internal Revenue Bureau in the Treasury Department.

Public Roads Administration in the Public Works Agency.

The Federal Trade Commission, the Works Progress Administration and the Civil Service Commission also deal with special phases of Forestry.

Among the emergency units set up in the Forest Service are the Prairie States Forestry Project (1934) and the Northeastern Timber Salvage Administration (1938).

far private owners may go in involving the state or the nation in future losses, so that they—a selfish few—may have a rich and immediate profit.

In the meantime, it should be clear that our last stands of spruce, western red cedar, and redwood are not a renewable resource, and are much more than a material resource. Majestic even in their lacerated state, they are a spiritual possession, and their destruction is nothing short of invasion of a sanctuary.

When President Franklin D. Roosevelt, opposing selfish and short-sighted interests, removed a spectacular part of the choicest stands from cutting by establishing the Olympic National Park, he erected another national landmark of conservation in the recognition of public rights against private exploitation.

There was a time when we blinded ourselves with the thought that our forest resources were inexhaustible. That was a time when it was possible to cut over state after state and move on to new slaughter. Today we know that with the disappearance of the forest all kinds of evil results follow.

So far as the forester is interested in the general scheme of conservation—and his interest is large—his main attention should be directed toward the avoidance of waste. It will never be possible to bring about the ideal of sustained yield if we permit a wholly unnecessary drain through prodigal commercial usages, or if the forestry interests fritter away their strength in extraneous ventures. It is well that leading men in the profession occasionally call attention to this, as for example Assistant Forester Herbert A. Smith did in his "State Accomplishments and Plans" section of *A National Plan for American Forestry* (Senate document 12, 1933):

WHITHER NOW?

The Roosevelt [Theodore] conservation movement had to do with, primarily, the great basic natural resources of the country. Its concern was for the main foundations underlying and supporting the economic life and material welfare of the Nation. To the end that the Nation might long endure as a great power in the family of nations and as a happy and prosperous people, the conservation movement sought to assure the perpetuation, through wise and far-sighted use, of the natural resources capable of perpetuation, and the husbanding through wise use of the wasting resources.

In the White House conference of 1908 and the work of the Roosevelt Conservation Commission which grew out of it, a classification of natural resources was made under the four heads of minerals, lands, waters, and forests. Some of the State conservation departments tended to follow along the line suggested by this general conception.

In a way, this was a revival of a trend which had appeared in some states in the very earliest stages of the forestry movement. But in the popular mind conservation rapidly drifted away from the basic conception of the Roosevelt movement and associated itself with such things as the protection of wild life, landscape, scenic and natural wonders, and outdoor recreational opportunities; not rational and far-sighted development of the best economic potentialities of material resources, but holding the despoiler in check and turning aside the march of civilization in the interest of the nature lover and of nature herself, or in the interest of sport and enjoyment of life in the open. A form of organization based on the idea that this is what conservation means has sometimes had an unfortunate effect upon forestry work, by placing it in association with activities of a different purpose and in charge of men whose background, interests, and training do not well fit them to understand the problems of forestry.

This is an important statement and nothing could be added to make it more forceful beyond pointing out that the popular mind's drift away from conservation realities was in many instances actively encouraged by opportunists in and out of office currying favor with the voter and his pocket-

119

book. The author is quite right in saying that the pursuit of such sidelines had an unfortunate effect upon forestry work.

The entire matter of conservation of our forests, as of all our resources, resolves itself into a question of good housekeeping. We fell heir to the greatest forest heritage known to human experience, but by and large we have turned out to be prodigal managers. We have frequently destroyed more than we are capable of using. Defense of such practices is being made in one part of the country, while in another, bankruptcy brought on by these malpractices is being faced.

Fantastically wasteful logging in Michigan, Wisconsin, and Minnesota, making all but a clean sweep of this once magnificent timber region, left in its wake a train of dire consequences. With the balances of nature upset, the people and the government face a terrific job of internal reconstruction. One would think that this would be a lesson to the states of Washington and Oregon. But is it? The magnificent stands of residual timber there is still available for cutting, selective or otherwise.

Ours is not a country of settled practices or traditions, or of static continuance of conditions. We are too young, the country is too large, to care much what happens in the future.

In order to preserve what remains of our forest heritage, the individual states must take prompt action. A survey of their condition has been made. Practical advice on the basis of long years of experience can be had from the Forest Service.

State rights have always found vociferous protagonists. Of state duties less has been said. Here, then, is an opportunity to assume a state duty and protect a state right. There is hardly a state, even including the few which have earnestly devoted themselves to sound forestry practices, which could not profitably enlarge their state forests or proceed with the building of forest tree nurseries where there are none.

But the work must not stop with the states. It must be taken up by counties and by municipalities. Indeed, there is a golden opportunity to build up small forests for material profit in the long run and as a source of joy and gratification to the people during its planting and growth.

Waiting for trees to renew themselves naturally will not do. Orderly forest stands hardly ever come about by themselves. It is late, but not too late, to organize tree growing in earnest. Young trees should be set out—not by the hundred thousands, but by the millions. Their growth must be watched carefully. Individually and collectively, we must assert our willingness and capacity to make restoration for lost values abstracted in less enlightened days.

We still speak of the public domain, and are justly proud of it, but that domain is only a fraction of what it once was. Because of past profligacy, our generation is face to face with a new task. We must work to build up a new public domain, which, added to the one we fortunately still possess, will in due time return happiness, stability, safety, and beauty to our land.

Forests have a higher and wider mission than merely to supply wood. Forests, lakes, streams, mountains, fertile valleys all belong together. Without them there would be little of human happiness or aspiration left. To preserve them, even the hard road will not seem too hard.

4. LAND

CHAPTER XII

SWEET LAND

SWEET land of liberty—dust storms, floods, submarginal lands, social unrest. These bear testimony to the terrific abuse which we as a people have given that sweet land.

It is good that deep down in our being we do take pride in the common possession and common achievement of our lavish land. Without the existence of this emotion, at times reaching the fervor of a passion, it would have been wholly impossible to win sufficient followers to the cause of conservation.

Compared with overpopulated Europe, America offered the early immigrant more light, more air, more space, and more opportunities. Here, in spite of sore disappointments and happy to have escaped his former hopeless existence, he looked forward with unfailing optimism to his new-found freedom and the opportunities it afforded. Here, with others from many lands, he helped work out a common destiny. Here, even in colonial days, the economic and social levels were higher than in the rest of the world, just as they are today.

Out of such circumstances rose the spirit of affection for the land, and with it a justifiable pride. For, in spite of all our backsliding, collectively, we did achieve one of the most astounding phenomena in the history of man—the conquest of a continent—and with it the building of these United States.

But the price we paid for our colossal achievement was equally colossal in heedless waste; and these many misdeeds have unsettled our body politic.

This is the situation we are in today, and it is providential that the conservation movement has produced a large and capable array of devoted talent, perfected in the theory and practice of treating our economic body as well as our social soul.

Our huge national heritage of land comprises nearly two billion acres, now populated by more than one hundred and a quarter million inhabitants. Let us take a look at it.

At the time of the arrival of the first white settlers on our shores, this vast land supported, according to some estimates, a slender Indian population of perhaps not more than two per cent of our present numbers. Their way of life required a larger acreage for subsistence than is needed under the white man's method of production. Since they were completely dependent upon nature and had no storage facilities, their range had to be wider.

Sir Arthur Keith estimates that a band of fifty Indians would require a hundred square miles of fertile land for subsistence. It could, he said, quadruple its numbers by cultivating even a hundredth part of its territory, while, if it merely stripped the land of its resources without replacing them, it remained stationary.

Dr. Hinsdale of the University of Michigan declared that

SWEET LAND

the Indians were the first and most scrupulous conservators. The white man changed all this.

In 1877 the grand total of venison shipments in Michigan during the two short months in which the weather permitted the transportation of deer was 1,070,000 pounds, of which 850,000 were shipped outside the state. This slaughter totals for a sixty-day season 10,700 carcasses. In one season 6,000 pounds, or three tons, of game birds, mostly partridges, were shipped from one city of 10,000 inhabitants alone. From the nesting place of pigeons . . . in Newaygo, Oceana, and Grand Traverse counties, in 1875, were shipped to outside market 1,000 tons, or 2,000,000 pounds, of young "squabs"; while not less than 200,000 dozen, or 2,400,000, birds were entrapped and shipped to all parts of the United States and England. . . .

A party of two gentlemen and two ladies who encamped upon a stream for about a fortnight caught 3,000 graylings, 2,000 of which were taken to Chicago, the other 1,000 not being in sufficiently good state of preservation to be transported. Another party from Chicago caught, during an expedition of four weeks, 5,000 graylings. The grayling is today almost an extinct fish in Michigan waters.

This kind of inhuman slaughter went on every season for many years.

During colonial times, land grants in large blocks were made by the Sovereign. They became either corporate or proprietory colonies. Among the former were the Virginia Company of London, the Council of New England and its successor in the person of a royal Governor, as well as Rhode Island and Connecticut. Among the latter, the so-called proprietory colonies, which finally reverted to the Crown, Maryland, Pennsylvania, and Delaware were still proprietory at the outbreak of the Revolution, having been restored to the proprietors after reversion. In the nature of things, these

127

ventures were highly speculative, and lent themselves to all kinds of practices—good, when high-minded and able administrators like Penn and Oglethorpe prevailed; evil, when the Crown's favorites gave reign to their insatiable cupidity.

After the termination of the Revolutionary War, a group of New Englanders, largely veterans of that war, formed the Ohio Company of Associates for purchase and settlement of lands on the Ohio River. This action hastened the passage by Congress of the Northwest Ordinance of 1787, which had as its purpose the cession of western lands held through royal charter by the old colonial states, thereby straightening out the tangled skein of land possession. According to Thomas Donaldson in *The Public Domain*, the territory so ceded by the original states to the United States amounted to 259,171,787 acres, which area represented the extent of the public domain before 1803.

Great additions to this were made in later years through purchases from France, Spain, Mexico, and Russia. If we exclude the latter, representing the Alaska Purchase, according to the report of the Public Land Commission of 1903, no less than 1,441,436,160 acres accrued.

The entire process of occupation of this vast territory was accomplished in less than a century. A glance at the land laws reveals the creation of a system meant to satisfy the land hunger of the increasing number of settlers. Although an earnest effort was made to be done with feudal practices of land tenure, based on the desire to have free men live and thrive on their own land, the system had, generally speaking, been one of uninterrupted failure—thanks to those who did yeoman's service in spreading the theorem that all our vast public domain should come into private hands; and to the

Large spruce and cedar trees near the old Olympus Ranger Station. The tree on the left is a spruce

Sugar pine trees in the Carl Inn Tract of which 7,200 acres are to be added to Yosemite National Park, California. These trees, on the western boundary of the park, are hundreds of years old and reach a height of over 200 feet and a diameter of 9 feet

Deep Erosion. The Land Seeks the Sea

A large part of the iron ore used in American steel mills comes from the Lake Superior region. This photograph shows an open pit mine in the Mesabi Range

Photo George A. Grant, Courtesy National Park Service

The Grand Tetons, as seen from near the old Elk-Grovont post road, east of Deadman's Bar

Courtesy the Department of Conservation, State of Indiana

Lake Michigan at the Indiana Dunes State Park

Panorama of Irrigated Lands, Grand Valley Reclamation Project, Colorado

Boulder Dam, the World's Highest Dam

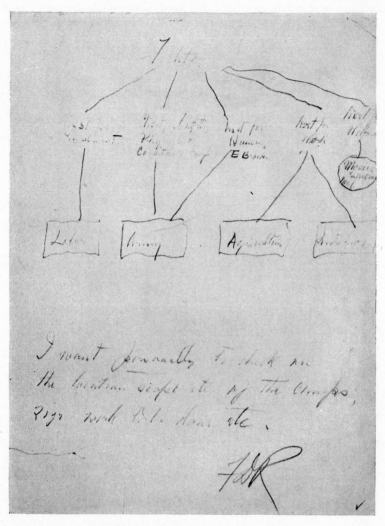

The President's Sketch of the C. C. C.

Mixed Sitka spruce, western hemlock, Douglas fir and western red cedar stand typical of the forest of the Olympic Peninsula, in the state of Washington. This photo was taken on the Quinault Indian Reservation near the Olympic Highway, several miles west of Quinault Lake

loose manner in which our land laws were executed, making possible quick and handsome returns to speculators and gamblers who put a blight on future healthy growth and development.

Pointed reference to this pitiful situation is made by Charles and Mary Beard in *The Rise of American Civilization*:

While the democracy of the east was attending Barnum's Circuses and museums, and intellectuals were discussing strictures on American culture by foreign travelers, alert pioneers and the agents of far-sighted capitalists on the distant frontier were enclosing, slashing, burning, and despoiling, without let or hindrance, national property that had been bought with the blood or the money of the whole country. While orators were loudly praising American institutions, members of Congress and high administrative officials were continuously engaged in land speculation, and it was a rare estate of generous proportions that was not tainted with irregularity in its acquisition. With feverish haste, this sequestration of the public domain went on unabated until, at the close of the nineteenth century, all the arable land had been given away and most of the timber and waste land had been transformed into private property. In such an urgency, the few scientists, who pointed out the perils bound to flow from a devastation of natural resources, could make little impression on hard-headed men of affairs acquiring or enjoying, or on the vast mass of voters absorbed as ever in their fated routine.

Under the laws of the last two decades of the eighteenth century, land sales netted the government approximately 75 cents per acre. Next came the General Land Acts, providing for public sale at not less than $2.00 per acre. In 1820, this price again was reduced to $1.25 per acre. Altogether there were thus sold 182,515,289 acres.

The next huge portion to pass from government to private ownership—a total of 27,361,836 acres—was sold under the General Pre-emption Law. Under this law, first enacted in 1841, 160 acres of land could be pre-empted by individuals without ready cash but with the intention of final payment and settlement. In spite of its praiseworthy intentions, this law nevertheless lent itself to land speculation and fraud. After the repeal of the private sale law in 1889, those who wished to acquire large tracts found loopholes in the Pre-emption Law by which more than the permitted 160 acres could readily be bought. With the assistance of dummy entries, and by taking advantage of a six-month payment clause, there was nothing to hinder a real owner from having such land—sometimes of considerable acreage—transferred to him after the "settler" had received his patent.

Another attempt to cheapen the price of lands for the benefit of actual settlers and for adjoining farms was made under the so-called Graduation Act. It worked no better than preceding ones, but during its eight years of existence 25,696,420 acres were sold under the previous minimum of $1.25 per acre.

The Homestead Act, passed in 1862, is perhaps the most important of all the land laws. It came during the Civil War and served expeditiously to supply bona fide settlers with new land. Pitfalls of abuse were not avoided under this law either, for it contained a provision for a commutation after six months' residence by the payment of $1.25 per acre, it being understood that the bona fide settlers received the patent without cost, after five years of residence. Briefly, the law was used by unscrupulous parties to add to their private holdings. Many such commuted parcels afterwards were found to be part of somebody's cattle or sheep ranch or timber holdings. According to land-office records, 115,124,295 acres have been patented under the homestead laws.

A number of other laws followed, but the next one of real significance was the Timber Culture Act of 1873. Under this law, in addition to 160 acres of homestead land, one could acquire a like amount, provided that at least ten acres of timber were planted and raised for a period of ten years. Knute Nelson in his "Summary of the Most Important Land Laws" records the presence of fraud and speculation as the result of this law.

The Timber and Stone Act of 1878 followed—with some dire consequences to Uncle Sam's pocketbook. This Timber and Stone Act provides that land may be sold at the minimum price of $2.50 per acre. Aside from the fact that the word minimum was changed to mean maximum, the main result of the Timber and Stone Act was the transfer of large tracts of timber to private individuals and corporations, at next to no cost. Without this law, past and existing timber empires would likely not have come into existence.

In making his report on this law to the National Conservation Congress, H. H. Schwartz has this to say:

This law has resulted in the sale of over 12,000,000 acres of valuable timber lands, of which fully 10,000,000 acres were transferred to corporate or individual timber land investors by the entry men. These lands brought to the people or general government a gross sum of $30,000,000. At the date of sale they were reasonably worth $240,000,000. The profit of over $200,000,000 went, not to the needy settlers engaged in subduing the wilderness, but to the wealthy investors. Not over a fractional part of one per cent of the timber purchased from the United States, under this act, is held, consumed or even cut by the men and women who made the entries.

There followed the Desert Land Acts, which in turn increased respect for law as little as did the Military Bounties Acts. The grant of vast acreage in the form of subsidies to railway, canal, wagon-road, and river improvement companies forms one of the most amazing studies in governmental mismanagement. Abuse of the law, through fraud, which was undoubtedly started with the best of intentions, has removed a total of 123,718,338 acres.

It is unfortunate that whenever we touch land deals we run into land steals. Unhappily the general public, in this as well as in other matters of public conduct, has not the slightest sense of abhorrence of corruption in high and low places.

A more hopeful picture is presented in the next grouping —showing the acreage turned over to the states. First, we have the amount of grants made for educational purposes. This began with the turning over of Section 16 in each township for common school purposes. Grants for seminaries and universities followed. Altogether, the amount for furthering education now totals 83,800,269 acres.

It is enlightening to see what happened to these acres after they passed into the state's hands. Some states disposed of them in short order, and at a low price. Other states kept them until they became of value. Van Hise reports that the probable future value of lands still owned by Minnesota University will not be less than $40,000,000, whereas, in Wisconsin, where university and agricultural lands were disposed of at the minimum price, a total of less than $600,000 was realized. The same author makes an interesting reference to the purchases by Ezra Cornell of governmental agricultural land script issued by the state of New York, located largely in the state of Wisconsin.

There followed, in 1862, a grant equal in importance to that made to the universities. This provided land for the establishment of agricultural and mechanical colleges, and had the most far-reaching consequences. Presented by Justin Smith Morrill of Vermont, it is known as the Morrill Act, and was signed on July 2, 1862, by President Lincoln. It had previously been approved by Congress in 1859, but was vetoed by President Buchanan. The institutions, "primarily devoted to instruction in agriculture, mechanics, and military science" established by Morrill Act grants, came to be known as land-grant colleges. To the elect, they appeared as nothing more than colleges for "blacksmiths and farmers." The common acceptance of science in agriculture has largely been brought about today by these land-grant colleges, working with the Department of Agriculture and disseminating their knowledge into the farthest reaches of their states.

The total for land disposed of to the states for all purposes—use and resale included—is in excess of 150,000,000 acres.

Today, the United States still owns 430,343,395 acres. Of this total, the chief items are public domain—220,180,090 acres; national forests—145,843,707 acres; national park areas—9,288,609 acres; and Indian lands—52,142,046 acres.

Our interest centers on the 220,180,090 acres remaining in the public domain, and on its contemplated use by the Federal government.

According to Paul W. Gates of the Land Policy Section

of the A.A.A., this remaining public domain is only a fragment of the vast area once included under this classification —yet it represents about one-fifth of our total land area, exclusive of Alaska, and, in terms of space, exceeds in area the total for Germany, France, Italy, Belgium, Holland, Switzerland, Denmark, Austria, Hungary, and Albania. Needless to say, all of the valuable agricultural land, most of the best mineral land, and a majority of the potential power sites, have long since passed into private ownership.

By far the largest part of the 220,180,090 acres—actually about 166,000,000 acres—consists of lands unreserved and unappropriated as of June, 1934. This vast region, previously subject to entry, has since been withdrawn by Executive Order, pending classification and determination as to its best use.

In that, we have hope. At last—if belatedly—the toil of far-sighted conservators, from Major J. W. Powell on down to the First National Conservation Association, has borne fruit. By classification before disposal, we have reason to believe that what remains of our vast public domain will be disposed of intelligently—in ways of benefit to the many, not merely the few.

CHAPTER XIII

OUR NATIONAL MEAL TICKET

WHEREVER we touch the matter of land use we find unbelievable disorder because of the manner in which private and corporate interests alike have succeeded in thwarting real progress. It is one of the inglorious chapters of our national history.

The historic attitude toward any given area was to rush in and develop and exploit it. The entire settlement of the country in waves and waves, as Frederick Jackson Turner described it, was one of planless rush. Of course, this method helped rapid expansion and development, but it skimmed off most of the cream, and it never took into consideration future development or future needs.

Under the circumstances, it was hopeless to warn against the consequences of such extravagance, because there was more land and more wealth still untouched. But in the last decade of the past century we came to the geographic limit of our resource, we began to feel the pinch, and now we must make readjustment in our methods of land use—not from choice, but from necessity.

All kinds of land troubles have risen to plague us, for we have abused nature so outrageously that we find ourselves in difficulty from one end of this great resource to the other.

Submarginal land, long familiar to older civilizations, is

a newcomer to our midst. These are generally thinly popu-lated areas which have so far deteriorated as to make culti-vation nearly worthless and the costs of providing adequate schools and roads excessive. It has been estimated that there are now 75,000,000 acres of such lands from which the popu-lation should be removed to a more favorable location.

Dust storms and floods play such dramatic parts in soil erosion that the layman often forgets that there are still other insidiously stealthy factors involved in the matter of land productivity versus soil depletion.

State authorities in the Great Lakes district, wondering what to do with the steadily mounting burden of tax-delin-quent land, are becoming bitterly congnizant of the main cause—the ruthless exploitation of our once magnificent timber resources.

No longer are we facing an academic theory. Today the urgency of our necessity is revealed in the Copeland Report, *A National Plan for American Forestry* (U. S. 73rd Con-gress, First Session), which states that because "most of the devastated forest lands which have become or are becoming tax delinquent will stay in public ownership whether they are wanted or not. Some form of public management must therefore be devised unless these lands are to be permanently non-productive."

When this same report suggests a possible reversion of 6,000,000 acres to public ownership within the next decade, it is probably understating its case. Michigan has already acquired title to 2,000,000 acres of tax-delinquent land— with 3,000,000 more in the offing. Over two-thirds of these exist in the old forest and cut-over counties.

The situation in Wisconsin and Minnesota is no better,

where in January, 1931, nearly 7,000,000 acres of land were delinquent. This represents forty-four per cent of the total taxable area.

The same trend exists in other parts of the country. It takes more than gentle persuasion to stop the lumber interests from abusing their property in the Pacific Northwest or in certain southern states and, through this abuse, creating within measurable time the same consequences of semi-bankruptcy that the Lake States are suffering from today.

What is to be done about it?

The old methods of governmental laxity or worse yet political corruptness will no longer serve. State and federal action is urgently needed. Instead of more politics, we have to find more policies. To those who can see, it must have become increasingly clear that property rights carry with them property duties. A new principle of land use must be evolved, on the basis of a better understanding of how deeply present abuse has damaged the commonwealth and wasted a great part of the common patrimony.

A consideration of the losses in general brings us to that of organic matter lost through cultivation of crops and use of pasture areas. Of the total losses of 70 per cent from harvested areas, 28.6 per cent is removed by crops and 40.3 per cent by leaching and erosion. From the remaining 30 per cent of organic matter which is lost from pasture areas, 18.6 per cent is removed by grazing and 12.3 per cent by leaching and erosion.

Just as Major Powell is considered today not only one of the great benefactors but one of the pathfinders in our economy of land use, so will a grateful posterity consider the devoted labors of Hugh Hammond Bennett, Chief of the

United States Soil Conservation Service. It seemed incomprehensible to him that we had so blindly neglected the importance of the topsoil with its vital function of a biochemical factory, staffed by incessantly laboring beneficial micro-organisms, and charged with the duty of returning decaying vegetable matter into available plant food.

The top few inches of soil [he says] often is higher in content of phosphorus and lime than the layers below; it is neutral or alkaline, where the sub-surface material is strongly acid. This is due to basic constituents brought up from below and concentrated in this surface layer through the medium of decomposing leaves and grass. . . . Experiments at the erosion stations (Soil Conservation Service) are showing not only large decreases in the productive capacity of land following the washing away of the soil, but even impairment of the quality of some of the products grown.

Scientifically, the facts of this conditioning and reconditioning process are well known. What is needed is a fuller popular appreciation that nothing—not even a spear of grass—could exist on top of the earth without the wonderful work constantly going on within the tenuous top layer of our precious soil.

That is the wealth we are destroying every day! That is the material we are sending down, mountain size, into the Mississippi delta. That is the material we pile up in reservoirs, subject to the havoc of wind and weather.

Russell Lord cites a hill in the Piedmont region that has been scoured bald in twenty years, a hill formerly covered with an estimated six or seven inches of rich top soil. Figuring that topsoil is formed from subsoil at a rate no faster than six hundred years to the inch, he says that it would take the weather at least 3,600 years to spread and stabilize a six-inch topsoil blanket on that hilltop, and it took only twenty years of indifferent farming to end and remove it. Soil that it took at least 3,600 years to make went off in about twice as many days.

Erosion, of course, is not solely responsible for the deterioration of our national soil. Even in those places where there is no appreciable loss from erosion, soil may easily become less and less productive through the removal or exhaustion of valuable elements.

The land furnishes us with food of all kinds—meats, milk and milk products, vegetables and fruits. It also provides our protective covering—wool, leather, and cotton, and, to a large extent, it still furnishes material for our housing and the means for heat and cooking. Of all of these, food is foremost. But before we can feed our own bodies, we must feed the plants that serve us.

In the course of their growth, plants remove organic matter from the earth, the most important elements being nitrogen, potassium, and phosphorus. Nitrogen, needed in large quantities by the human system, is derived from our plant and animal food, which in turn must get it from the earth. Vast quantities of nitrogen are destroyed by the pernicious habit of single-cropping. Setting woods on fire is another, and this is one of the quickest ways of removing nitrogen. While this practice is still popular in the state of Florida, there are signs of awakening to the damage being done.

A boundless supply of nitrogen exists in the atmosphere, and science has succeeded in bringing it down to earth. This helps the farmer a little, the manufacturer of high explosives more. The allusion to such plants as clover, alfalfa, beans, and peas as "vegetable dynamite" rests upon their capacity to draw nitrogen from the air, and to make the necessary combination with the other elements in the soil, the work of transformation again being done by bacteria. The realization of all this has greatly helped to advance the beneficial practice of rotation of crops.

Potassium in soluble form, to replace that lost in the process of cultivation, has been obtainable largely from German deposits in the past. However, we have native rock in sufficient quantity to satisfy our needs, and fortunately within easy reach.

The huge losses of phosphorus, partly through the natural pursuits of agriculture, and partly through thoughtless dissipation, is a great source of danger not alone to agriculture, but to human life itself, for phosphorus must be considered the delimiting force in soil productivity.

The infertility of Asiatic fields is largely one of deficiency in phosphorus. Our own soils have become so seriously depleted in phosphorus that in many places phosphate compound must be used as fertilizer. Tests made as long as thirty years ago in the Central West show an astonishing increase in crop returns after the use of raw phosphate.

The chief factors in the loss of land fertility due to the absence of phosphorus are the natural abstraction from the soil by the crop, the leaching and erosion of the ground, and a disregard of the value of stable and barnyard manure. For this last reason, dairy farming is much more advantageous to the soil than grain farming. In experiments conducted by Whitson and Stoddard at the University of Wisconsin Agricultural Experimental Station, it was revealed that on a Wisconsin dairy farm of one hundred acres the net annual loss of phosphoric oxide was 30 pounds. On a Wisconsin grain farm of the same size the loss was 615 pounds. The importation from the flour mills of Minnesota of phosphate-carrying bran feed made the difference.

This disposition of bran throws an amusing sidelight on the vagaries in the use and preparation of our natural food materials. Bran piles up in these mills by its removal from the grain. Removed with the bran is also about 80 per cent of the phosphorus contained in it. Now a large proportion of our people subsist on potatoes and wheat as their most common food. Both potatoes and "refined" wheat are highly deficient in the needed phosphate ration. As a result of this care taken in removing the bran from the grain, there is a constantly growing need to find other ways of getting bran into our diet. America seems to have a perverse desire to solve her diet problem the hard way.

In the days when the United States was a large exporter of grain and meat products, large quantities of phosphorus left the country for good. Two of the most extravagant crops in the extraction of phosphorus are cotton and tobacco. Whitson finds that the loss in tobacco farming, in addition to the amount extracted by the crop itself, is twelve times as great as that with grain. Cotton takes a similar toll.

A further loss of phosphorus is occasioned by our handling of sewage. Reference to the nuisance of stream pollution has been made elsewhere. In this connection, it should be pointed out that, bad as stream pollution is and adversely as it affects public health and offends against common decency, equally great is its prodigal waste of valuable material. Stables and barnyards are individual offenders. Farmers have never thought of manure as a particular asset. Nearly one-half of it, both liquid and solid, not only is wasted but, through infiltration, adds to the contamination of our underground water supply.

Under such prevailing circumstances, it is in the national interest to protect the high-grade phosphate rock deposits in the country. Further exploitation should be held within reasonable bounds. Aside from the southern beds in South Carolina, Florida, and Tennessee, there are still astonishingly large deposits of phosphorus rock available in the western phosphate fields.

After coal and iron, our phosphates rank as our most precious mineral heritage. Their judicial use and preservation, therefore, is the most pressing and far-reaching problem in the entire field of agricultural conservation.

One factor that makes improvement in the agricultural conservation picture difficult is the prevalence of farm tenancy and share-cropping. The return of millions to the soil during the depression aggravated an already ominous condition. A further increase may swamp the entire rural economy.

To understand the institution of farm tenancy, it is necessary to remember the nature of private property in land, whose foundation is the common-law theory that private property and land are held subject to the rights of the sovereign. The sovereign in this country, organized society, retains certain rights; for example, the right of taxation, the right of eminent domain, and other policing powers which are calculated to protect the public welfare.

These limitations, however, have been asserted more in the cities than in the country. And the noticeable shift in public opinion in the direction of further restrictions of use by the owner, is still confined to closely settled areas, where the imposition of such restrictions is in the interest of public health and safety.

On the other hand, the owner of non-urban land has so far enjoyed almost unlimited use and abuse of his possession. There are no restrictions to keep him from cutting off all timber, from wasting soil fertility, from exploiting mineral resources, and in many other ways exhausting the wealth of the land. Although that situation is bad enough under resident ownership, it has been found that excesses are increased where absentee ownership prevails.

During the colonial period, the accepted view was that the land was owned by the Crown, which, in turn, granted rights to large colonizing companies. It was a convenient way for the English propertied class, interested in these companies, to obtain large tracts of land and have them operated through the labor of a poor immigrant working class—if not as slaves, then as indentured servants, tenants, or agricultural laborers. This was a remnant of feudal practices which were wiped out during the Revolutionary period.

But farm tenancy persisted in spite of the Federal land system aimed at promoting individual settlement through grants of land and low-priced sales. From the time of the first land ordinance in 1785, up to the Homestead Act of 1862, unsettled lands were disposed of in relatively large tracts. This in itself was conducive to tenancy. Specialized crop production and commercialized farming operations, especially in the South, fostered its growth. In the North, commercialized farming probably had its greatest development after settlement had reached the plains areas.

The census of 1880 for the first time showed the number of tenant farmers. To the surprise of many, it was ascertained that 26 per cent of the farmers were tenants. Our national land policy, intended to put free land into the hands of free farmers, had failed to this extent. In 1880 there were 4,008,907 farmers in the country. By 1930 the figure had increased 57 per cent, or to 6,288,648. During the same period, tenancy increased 160 per cent, from 1,024,601 to 2,664,365.

These 6,288,648 farm operators were classified in four major groups:

1. Full owners, owning all the land they operate.

2. Part owners, who own only part of the land they operate and rent part of it.

3. Managers, farmers who operate farms or ranches for the owner, receiving wages or salaries.

4. Tenants, farmers who own none of the land they operate.

It is important to find out what this increasing land tenancy is doing to the land, as well as what the land is doing to those human souls who work, and frequently slave, on it.

The American people have a decided propensity for nomadic existence. This coming and going, this old spirit of pioneering and adventure, has done great things for the development of the country; but it has also injected the elements of instability which make themselves disagreeably felt in the years of maturity.

It is natural that tenants, as a rule, remain only a short time. It isn't their land, after all, and perhaps somewhere else there are better chances waiting. Under these circumstances, it is not likely that the tenant or his family will become interested in the social or economic life of the community. He will not care to join the rural institutions, in the discussion of problems, and so forth. He stands apart. What interest can he have in keeping up the fertility of the soil, or maintaining the buildings in good condition, or even watching for the beginning of erosion?

Henry A. Wallace, when he was Secretary of Agriculture, said: "We have been talking about the evils of farm tenancy in this country for a great many years. It is high time that America faced her tenant situation openly and pursued a vigorous policy of improvement."

Whether measured by the numbers of farmers or the amount of farm land operated, farm tenancy in the United States is almost on a par with farm ownership. According to the 1930 census, tenancy made up 42 per cent of all farmers, operated 31 per cent of all land in farms, and cultivated 42 per cent of all harvested crop land in the United States. If we add to this group the 656,755 farmers who rented part of the land they farmed, we find that 53 per cent of our country's farmers rented some or all of their land, and 44 per cent of all land farmed was under lease.

It is not necessary to do away with the tenant system. But it is imperative that the system be sanitated. The present anarchy in land use must be superseded by a better order; and this order, as common sense would dictate, must not begin with the share cropper but with the owner of the land. The fact that he delegates, through the instrument of a farm lease, extensive rights to the party of the second part must under no circumstances release him from his responsibility to organized society. Absolute ownership still is vested in the state, and through the use of its police power it may—in the public interest—correct existing evils.

Progressive ruination of the soil does not stop with the collapse of farming. If left unchecked, it would some day reduce the whole nation to want and misery.

In an article in the December, 1937, issue of *The American Mercury*, called "Death from the Soil," which every person in the United States could read with profit—for every person, no matter what his condition or station, is affected by the rapidly advancing and most insidious destruction of the soil—Dr. Paul B. Sears pointed out that the soil is our national meal ticket. Already, he said, the earned standard of living of the average American farmer has slipped behind that of the European peasant, and we are headed at full speed on a path that has brought destruction to others as well-meaning and energetic as ourselves.

City people are not concerned because they don't know what is happening until it is too late, and the plague of high food and clothing sets in. But even this is seen only as an effect. The real underlying cause—the diminishing of our nation's soil value—is not even dreamed of by the vast majority.

Nor must we forget [continued Dr. Sears] that in destroying the soil we let ourselves in for trouble other than agricultural decline. The dark top layer of virgin soil, rich in absorptive organic matter, is a prime factor in restraining the destructive hand of floods. A ground deprived of this protection loses water from ten to thirty times faster than it did before. When it comes to flood control, the soft and sponge-like humus is as staunch an ally as hard walls of concrete . . . the top soil and its covering of vegetation no longer stand guard for us. Instead, our great river cities bear the direct impact of washing waters. . . . Soil and water are accurate measures of the abundance of life. In a sense the relationship of the two is a sliding one, for the scarcer the one the greater need for the other. . . . We have mentioned the curse of flood and drought, but we have said nothing about another and equally great aspect of the water problem. To tell the truth, North America, like other continents before it, is drying out.

The best minds in the country for long years have been crying out against this self-willed pauperization. Laws and more laws have been passed. But not until this demand for more legislative action is changed into the will to stop such abuses will there be any change for the better. If we wish to remain a country of free institutions, happy, self-reliant, and prosperous, we ourselves as a people must act, and this means our urban population, particularly, for as Dr. Sears so pointedly declares: ". . . until Chambers of Commerce, Industrial Associations, and your civic bodies have the sense to see that they are in the same boat with the farmer, all the legislation in the world is not going to turn the trick."

CHAPTER XIV

NEEDED: A NEW ORDER

"AS NATURAL resources are for the benefit of man, the human resources must come first." This statement is frequently made when matters of conservation are discussed. It is the response of earnest, well-meaning people. There is only one drawback. It isn't true. As a matter of fact, human resources do not come first. They cannot, because there is no happy or fruitful life possible without the presence and conservation of natural resources in profuse variety. With land, as with all other resources, the lives of those who depend upon it will be enriched or impoverished in proportion to the care given it.

Unfortunately, the Federal government lacks adequate machinery to deal with land administration, and the same shortcomings that make themselves felt in other branches of conservation have become glaringly obvious danger signals in connection with our greatest of all resources—land.

At the present time, all land questions are handled, if they can be handled at all, by subordinate bureaus of the government. There is lacking a national receptacle which first receives, then co-ordinates, and finally puts into effect those findings.

The present course is and has been wasteful and ineffective. Specialists or bureau chiefs reduce the general importance of any problem to the need of the immediate matter in hand and, by so doing, remove the concrete universality of the problem from the field of vision.

Aside from such matters as erosion and exhaustion of the soil, drainage, irrigation, forests, grazing, Indian lands, or tax defaults, there are any number of interrelated factors that must be weighed in considering questions of land use. Among them, for instance, are its effect on cities, harbors, towns, waterways, highways, parks, or future recreational needs. Such complex and highly integrated problems of general land use cannot be covered—let alone be solved—except by a national policy for the conservation of the entire resource. Thus far this has not been done, and in consequence functional activities collide with each other, and we, as a nation, are the loser.

To remedy this, both city and country must recognize their individual roles and joint responsibility.

The country not only feeds and clothes the city, but created it in the first place, and by its surplus population keeps it going. From a mere 3 per cent of the total population 150 years ago, urban population has now risen to 56 per cent. The city does not increase on the basis of its birthrate. City families have grown smaller, and the older age groups larger. The maintenance and increase is furnished by the country. The depression exodus in the opposite direction, during the past ten years, when more than 3,000,000 persons left the city and returned to the country, was not a matter of free choice, and hence a new trend, but rather economic pressure pure and simple: starvation in the city versus subsistence in the country.

The usual complaint, that the cities absorb the country

149

population, that cities are overpopulated and that the country is underpopulated, is nothing but astigmatism on the part of the statistician. The fact is, rather, that the rural population remains relatively stationary, whereas the cities, with their multitudinous demands on trade and industry, absorb the increase of the population, as they must if they wish to maintain themselves.

Decentralization of industry and better distribution of finished products seems to be in the economic offing. But, even so, the industrial city will multiply by dividing itself. The relative position of farm versus city will likely remain the same, and what is henceforth required by way of agricultural products will largely be determined, as now, by the city population—by its number, its standard of living, and its general health and prosperity, with, of course, foreign trade as a lesser determinant.

The astounding picture of distribution of population in the United States can be presented in one pregnant sentence: 47,000,000 live on two-tenths of 1 per cent of our land, whereas 75,000,000 have to themselves 99.8 per cent of it (Census of 1930).

Someone has said that city dwellers pay so little attention to land because they have so little of it. That in itself is true enough; for cities and towns, with their highly concentrated populations, occupy but 12,000,000 out of a total of nearly 2,000,000,000 acres, or less than seven-tenths of 1 per cent. The exchange between producer and consumer is effected by a transportation system of lakes, rivers, railroads, and highways, of which the two last occupy 23,000,000 acres, or 1.1 per cent—this making a total of 1.8 per cent of our total national acreage with which the city dweller has direct contact.

We used to make invidious comparison when we said that the country was made by God and the city by man. The ensuing shortcomings in living conditions seem to have been noticed in recent years by the more fortunately situated city population, and in consequence we are meeting, contiguous to the city, with an entirely new movement, that of "suburbanization."

Unlike the European cities, where even now a good percentage of residence is maintained in business districts, the trend with us soon took the road of separation. The business district was in one place; the residential district in another. The city increased by "additions." As the city grew and the business district expanded, the residential quarters were simply shoved out to the periphery, leaving behind perfectly good if not elaborate residences, which, though too expensive to maintain, often served, as now, the commercial needs of the section. With each new shift of the residential population, new problems of schools, light, fuel, sewage disposal, and so forth all had to be solved. In the city itself, costs for services such as fire and police protection, water, gas, and light went on as before, but were relatively increased. The tendency to raze such buildings as could not be put to commercial use, and thus to lower the consequent tax charge, only worsened the situation.

Medieval cities, as centers of the guilds, were, in a measure, forerunners of the modern industrial city, but with this difference: the medieval city tried to organize and combine all the guilds and their activities in one city; the modern city

151

tries to specialize in that particular trade or industry for which local conditions seem best adapted. With this increase and development of industry comes further specialization, until the modern city is no longer producing things for its own or a narrowly confined consumption, but for the whole national market, and not infrequently for international consumption. Thus it becomes a potent factor in international exchange of values.

But, in the same measure as the city has improved the economic status, it has likewise sharpened the competition for its attainment. It has made higher demands on intelligence, energy, and efficiency. It has been said of the city that the tempo of thinking and acting is correspondingly increased as the population increases.

With the multiplied efforts of the city has come an elevation of the intellectual culture of the nation. Today the cities are the acknowledged leaders in the economic, intellectual, spiritual, and artistic life of a people. But they are also the seats of dissatisfaction and of established evils and wrongs.

There is cause for the existence of such evils and wrongs, but there is no necessity for their continuance. As soon as we are willing to reach for the underlying causes and change or remove them, we shall do away with undesirable or dangerous effects. This, for instance, has been done in the matter of public sanitation. The need for safe plumbing, sewers, garbage removal, medical inspections, and so forth was felt in the centers of population. The country would not have thought of it; there was not enough need for it. But the city, realizing its own insufficiency, corrected it.

NEEDED: A NEW ORDER

So again in time-honored fashion, the city leads, the country follows.

Unfortunately, we have not been similarly courageous in the handling of social ailments. In the matter of commercialized vice, for instance, we shut our eyes to the causes and have left hysteria, hypocrisy, and cowardice to deal with mere effects. In this and similar matters, we are everlastingly treating symptoms instead of diseases, attacking effects instead of causes, and thereby aggravating the malady.

Too little attention is paid to the furnishing of wholesome amusement and recreation; too little, above all, to the proper housing of vast numbers of our fellow citizens. The impartial majesty of law, as Anatole France said, speaking of similar conditions in his country, prohibits beggars and millionaires alike from stealing a loaf of bread or sleeping under the approaches to bridges.

Urban housing is one of our most troublesome problems; it must be solved, however, not only from the humanitarian standpoint of social justice, but also from the concurrent one of hygiene necessity, because slums and other blighted areas represent a horrible municipal liability.

That our cities are maladministered is openly admitted, except, of course, by those who profit by the existing chaos, and not infrequently by others who, on account of historic traditions, oppose fundamental changes.

City charters generally follow the form of the Federal government. They are faint tracings of the Constitution itself. In the beginning, that was well and good, for when the constitution was made we did not know the modern city. Today the peculiar dual system of legislative and administrative checks and balances has wrought havoc. Our cities are administered by politics to obtain spoils, not to obtain efficiency.

Of course, it is wholly absurd to proceed with the election of a new man and cast aside the old administrative machinery every four years. Occasionally a city has been successful in getting an able man for mayor—and what did he find? In the first place, that he was hemmed in by politics and hopelessly hampered by an antiquated system. Secondly, that he had so many checks and restrictions placed upon him that the best part of his program could be carried out only by making weakening compromises. Thirdly, his real usefulness would begin about the time his term of office expired.

The same unfortunate conditions govern the personnel of the various departments. It is a shameful waste to throw their expert knowledge—partly obtained at the taxpayer's expense—on the municipal scrap pile every four years.

We shall never have competent and efficient city government unless we buy it and pay for it, as we must pay for any service in proportion to its value. And not until we have a highly efficient and systematized administration can we hope to make the city the center and the fountainhead of communal interests.

Today we buy and pay for goods that are not delivered. It is for that reason that the people have to go into their pockets continually to pay individually or as groups for things that should be included in the general taxation and be provided for by the municipality, whether it be a policeman, street lighting, shelter house, public charity, or free milk station.

As we now have the city administered (if that expression be permissible at all), a municipality can never have funds enough for things that are plainly within its province; for it is a political body for political gain and not a business enterprise for the common good.

The city must buy water, electricity, gas, and steam, from corporate interests, and give away valuable rights of transportation, telephone, and other public service. In fact, if you look more closely, the city has given away all of those things which would be a source of income—water, electricity, gas, street railways, and so forth—and, because nobody wanted them, has had to retain all of those which are a dead expense, such as street cleaning, garbage removal, sewers, and so forth.

We are told by disinterested patriots that municipal ownership is a failure. Of course it is, and so would every merchant's business be a failure if he had a mind to turn it over to be managed by the same "experts" who seek our votes at election times.

To be the mayor of a city ought to be a vocation, instead of a matter of popular acclaim. The chiefs of the various departments should likewise be selected on account of their experience and knowledge, and the rules of civil service should be strictly applied to all city employees.

Stability of management, high-powered efficiency, thorough development of business organization in its most minute detail, a grasp of big things, and the exercise of economy in all are the requirements for success in private business. Is it not a dethronement of reason to suggest that these same peremptory demands should not, with like force, apply to public business? How long would any business last if it were conducted along political, instead of commercial, lines? Have you ever seen a tree live that was uprooted every four years? But that is precisely what we do to the tree of municipal administration.

We speak of democracy and the rule of the people, but we forget that democracy is an ideal that we have to fight for every day, and that the price, like that of liberty itself, is eternal vigilance.

In this connection, a careful reading of Meredith Nicholson's chapter on "Provincial Capital" in his book *The Provincial American* is not without profit. From it we may learn how to improve our modern status, not by abandoning old ideals, but by using them as building stones for a new temple of municipal salvation. In part, Mr. Nicholson says:

> The difficulties in the way of securing intelligent and honest city government have, however, multiplied with the growth of the city. . . . The more prosperous a city the less time have the beneficiaries of its prosperity for self-government. It is much simpler to allow politicians of gross incapacity and leagued with vice to levy taxes and expend the income according to the devices and desires of their own hearts and pockets than to find reputable and patriotic citizens to administer the business. Here as elsewhere the party system is indubitably at the root of the evil. Indeed . . . both the old political organizations feel that the loss of the city at a municipal election jeopardizes the chances of success in general elections. Just what effect the tariff and other national issues have upon street cleaning and the policing of a city has never been explained.

The explanation of this phenomenon, however, seems simple enough. When we complain that we rarely get first-class men to enter the City Council, we forget that these business and professional men cannot very well enter a council when they themselves, or at least their immediate friends, are interested in franchises worth millions that have to be protected. They can attend to the safeguarding of their interests much better from without than from within. For that reason, our businessmen are quite willing to lend their energy, experience, and actual knowledge to the improvement of libraries, educational institutions, hospitals, and other public or semi-public agencies because purse and patriotism are there in less danger of a collision.

It is absurd to think that in the twentieth century, when everything else must be intensely ordered, specialized, and classified in order to succeed, the biggest corporation of all, the municipality, should be allowed to run along in the haphazard, nonchalant, and jovial manner of a musical comedy.

Our patriotism, so far as our own great country is concerned, cannot be doubted. What we need to cultivate is the variety which, far from weakening our allegiance to the republic, would rather strengthen and deepen it—that is, local patriotism.

We must find the courage to effect a change for the better. The aggregate physical and moral health of a city depends on the contentment and happiness of its people. What we need is not vice crusaders or professional reformers, not fanatics who see harm and sin in every innocent amusement, but high-minded and big-hearted men and women who will make the city an abode of light and joy and justice. Order, once having supplanted disarray, would call into action for the common good those quiescent voices whose power for good has been submerged in the din of riotous derangement.

Thus will be created a better understanding not only of our immediate urban opportunities but of our interdependence with the country at large, which furnishes the city with sustenance through food and strength of man power.

On his side, the farmer, influential in state politics, either in his own right or as a pawn of contending economic urban interests, must learn that as a producer of surplus food stuffs, or other agricultural products, his own welfare is dependent upon the well-being of the consumer of large and small industrial centers. He must learn that interference with the freedom of the city in the long run means interference with his own well-being, a well-being constantly being improved as agriculture finds its due recognition and place.

Abraham Lincoln should be recognized as the patron saint of all field workers for agricultural improvement because, with the signing of the Morrill Act, he ushered in the dawn of scientific agriculture. Today we have agricultural colleges all over the country. In some states these are of college rank; in others, secondary schools. There are other gradations. Minnesota, for instance, maintains an agricultural high school in connection with the university. The ideal situation would be to introduce agricultural education in the rural schools, in order to give every boy and girl a chance to become conversant from youth up with the possibilities of farming on the basis of sound land use.

Most efforts in the past for the amelioration of unsatisfactory social conditions and environment have been directed toward urban youth. Boy Scouts, Girl Scouts, Campfire Girls, and denominational and other camps in which education was made pleasant followed each other in rapid succession. Little had been done for the rural youth because it was thoughtlessly held that country children could enjoy the country any time, while city children had been deprived of it.

I too held this narrow view until I appeared at a country meeting in Indiana to discuss the availability of a near-by area for state park purposes. I returned from that meeting, I hope, a better and certainly a wiser man.

The big hall was packed with eager youngsters, representing all the high schools in three counties. I regretfully explained that, since there was not much of beauty and character to preserve in the proposed park area, my inclination was to turn down the project. A young spokesman rose and replied. He spoke of the ambitions of all the assembled youngsters, of their love of their nation, their state, and their home. He drew a vivid picture of the dreariness and drabness of the surroundings. He thought that these young citizens would be a help or a hindrance in the future, depending upon the opportunities that were given them for a wider life and finer appreciation. He wound up in the best manner of a Roman orator and said, "The state tells us that there is nothing here of beauty or character to save and to preserve. Aren't we here?"

As a result of that telling argument, the park was established, with particular attention to the needs of rural youth. It has become tremendously popular and, strangely, too, a thing of beauty. It is now the center of 4-H club activities carried on by that intelligent group of agricultural field workers, the county agents.

The high social value of the 4-H clubs cannot be overestimated. In the first place their work follows scientific principles. It produces a keen sense of clean competition, and, being a little institute in itself, it promotes the inspirational outlook on a labor which otherwise is full of toil at best. Agricultural investigation and instruction cannot begin too early, to be followed later by agricultural extension on a scale even greater than we have come to know it today. The 4-H clubs supply the fundamentals with sugar coating.

And so both the country and the city work toward a new order—a new era—in which, recognizing a community of interests, and viewing the whole land as one large home, the inhabitants of each can take pride as members of one great family in the protection and cultivation of the soil which supports them all with the fruits of its bounty.

5. SCENERY

CHAPTER XV

UNBROKEN WILDERNESS

"WHY parks?" The question is frequently asked.
Parks are the dietetics of the soul. No matter how much we may do indirectly, by way of sports and athletics, for the body, the spiritual hunger and search for things hidden goes on. Man, Antaeuslike, feels the physical necessity of keeping in touch with nature; his soul seeks a haven of rest. This, in general, is the answer to the question: "Why parks?"

But in the case of our own great scenic parks, there is a further answer. We of today want to preserve for ourselves and for those of tomorrow significant examples of our natural wonders and wilderness, so that these may prove eternal fonts of American idealism on which to draw not only for inspiration, but for new appreciation of the roots of our American way.

Parks, by one name or another, have been popular in most ages. Babylon and Persia, Greece and Rome in their glory created environs of beauty and refinement—as often as not the luxurious self-expression of powerful rulers. The Middle Ages did not know parks in that sense. The Renaissance revived them and the Baroque and Rococo periods developed the formal and semi-formal gardens. Of the latter, here in our country, the Magnolia or—if a preference in

163

perfect things is permitted—the Middleton Gardens near Charleston, South Carolina, are priceless examples.

At all times a park seems to have been an enclosed tract of land; in early England it meant one containing wild beasts of the chase, and later on domesticated cattle as well. Parks were set aside by grant or prescription of the King. Eventually the use of the word extended to the grounds of a country house or mansion, including ornamental areas of woodland and pasture. In time, parts of large estates or of crown lands were organized into residential property or for public use. Examples of the latter are Hyde Park, once the manor of Hyde and part of Westminster Abbey, and Kensington Gardens, originally the grounds of Kensington Palace. The former often bear names taken from old country houses or mansions, such as Clapham Park or Addington Park.

The oldest direct reference to parks, as we have come to know them, was made by George Catlin, an American artist and traveler. In 1832, on ascending the Missouri and beholding part of the glory of the Yellowstone country, he wrote: "What a beautiful and thrilling experience for America to preserve and hold up to the view of future ages! A nation's park containing men and beasts, in all the wild and freshness of their nature's beauty."

Some forty years later, the members of the Washburn-Langford-Doane Yellowstone Expedition sat around a campfire, in the autumn of 1870, discussing the superlative scenery and the land of wonders they had just found. In the manner of the day they were making plans for dividing it among them for personal exploitation, when Cornelius Hedges injected a revolutionary thought. Instead of profiting personally by their discoveries, he said, why not endeavor to have the entire area set aside for the use and enjoyment of all the people? This thought was given instant approval. And so the Yellowstone wonderland, destined to become our first national park—the first, in fact, in the world—passed into the hands of the people.

"For the benefit and enjoyment of the people," reads the inscription on the great arch at the north entrance to Yellowstone National Park. What the inscription fails to add is the concurrent demand that the grounds and all they contain shall be preserved and retained in their natural condition. Stated specifically, in the language of the Act of March 1, 1872, establishing Yellowstone National Park, this demand was for "the preservation from injury or spoliation of all timber, mineral deposits, natural curiosities, or wonders within said park and their retention in their natural condition."

The difficult, and of course ceaseless, task of the National Park Service has been to harmonize these conflicting objects of our desire: use and preservation. Never were they more at variance than in our present parks.

While in our parks we seek surcease from the pace of an increasingly mechanized existence, and try to restore balance in soul and body, we must not forget that Nature's balance, too, must be maintained and restored in our surroundings, in spite of and often because of our transient desires and needs.

By limiting our demands, and thus helping to preserve the "yet unbroken wilderness" aspect of our parks, we not only help to insure increased spiritual values for ourselves in the superlative examples of natural grandeur and ineffable beauty, but we fulfill a great patriotic purpose. Nowhere in our country can the native-born and foreign-born alike listen to greater sermons on Americanism than in our parks. Nowhere can they gain a greater understanding of what it cost our forefathers of '76 to found the nation in which today we live with such ease and prosperity.

If by "wilderness" we mean the fortuitous residue now held in public ownership, another question looms up, namely: Is it our purpose to preserve intact—so far as that is possible—this wilderness residue, or are we proposing, in a manner, to make outdoor museum specimens out of this, that, or the other feature of these public parks?

"Wilderness" by definition means "a tract or region uncultivated and uninhabited by human beings." What we mean, in connection with our parks, is the preservation in its natural aspects of the area we have selected as a park, barring only the unavoidable elements of intrusion demanded by service to the visitor and provision for his physical comfort. For that reason, the idea of setting aside wilderness areas in state or national parks seems incongruous. If it is a real park—one of supreme beauty and interest—it must follow that the entire property should be treated, conserved, and, if necessary, brought back as much as possible to its natural condition; the human needs of service which today threaten the survival of such areas with their ever increasing demands, will in the nature of things take second place.

Thus, our attempt to recreate man by recreating an environment, if humbly approached, not only will bring us the satisfaction of having created havens for our errant, searching souls, but will enable us and future generations to see the America of today and tomorrow in true national perspective.

Between city and national parks there are the state parks. These are often so named without consideration of their actual condition or status, and are sometimes painfully reminiscent of Maria Edgeworth's lament in Walter Scott's time: "Just what would feed the cow is sufficient in Ireland to constitute a park."

As to the ideal of a state park, Yosemite with its scenic and inspirational values gives us a clue. Though now part of a great national park, it originally became the first designated state park when the government granted Yosemite Valley and Mariposa big trees to California in 1864.

In February, 1935, Secretary Ickes made a statement on state parks which, by implication, also fits national parks:

When state parks are more removed from crowded centers, if I had my way, I would foster and cherish the wilderness aspect of the areas. I hope as the states develop their own park systems, they will have to mind that citizens in time to come would like to know what the country in each state looked like before we civilized people came in and began to work our will on it.

Some of us remember the prospect half a century ago— twenty-eight days spent in travel over what could now be covered by air in a few hours—pack trains over mountainous and difficult terrain—time out for hunting, fishing, resting, and side trips—riding faint trails by compass and by instinct.

Even by train forty years ago it took two and one-half days to travel to Yosemite from San Francisco. Leaving in the morning one would change cars at Berenda for Raymond, stay overnight, and proceed on the next morning's stagecoach northeastward through Ahawohne, a lunch and relay station, to Wawona, arriving there after nightfall. Part of the next morning was devoted to seeing the "big trees," and then the stagecoach would rumble on, finding its tortuous way through Chinguapin Flats over the old Yosemite and Wawona turnpike, and come to a sudden halt at Inspiration Point. No one who has ever come upon the valley in this way could forget that picture!

Today, if rail travel is preferred, one leaves San Francisco by late sleeper, eats breakfast on the train, and arrives at the park in the forenoon.

Compared with 5,000 visitors coming by stagecoach or on horseback forty years ago, 539,728 arrived last year in 140,000 automobiles. Naturally the accommodation and servicing of such ever increasing numbers has put a tremendous strain not only on the landscape, but on the Park Service dedicated to preserving that landscape in its pristine naturalness.

With the creation of our first national park there entered unobserved, but certainly not premeditated, the issue of proper land use. Today every forward-looking state government, as well as the Federal government, knows that the conservation of its natural resources must include its scenery. Today the inspirational, the social, and, last but not least, the economic value of scenery is generally known, and will be increasingly put to good use, as the legislative and administrative errors of the past are corrected.

Parks are the show windows of conservation. Their use and abuse rest on the very principles of the use and abuse of land. In their proper care is exemplified the methods of well-ordered land use. It is therefore of vast importance that we see to it that in them preservation takes precedence over use.

To keep our magnificent heritage of scenery and wild life in such condition that Nature can carry out her laws, more thoughtful purists are needed—and fewer reckless expansionists and showmen.

CHAPTER XVI

HORSE-AND-BUGGY RULE

NO OTHER country on earth has a park system comparable in extent, numbers, or variety with our own, directed by the National Park Service. Fortunately, our government set aside these large and significant tracts in time to save them from private exploitation and spoliation. How great and ever present this danger is becomes apparent during nearly every session of Congress, when, even today, both private and corporate cupidity try to reach into these illustrious reservations for loot. Covetous, avaricious, and keenly alert, these evil forces have too often succeeded, owing to the lack of a Federal control agency.

Individuals, corporations, Representatives, and Senators who thus combine against the public weal should have monuments erected to them, properly inscribed—in the manner of the Chinese, who thus expose to public scorn their great malefactors.

The building, planning, and maintenance of all parks is so completely bound up with the public weal that we should eliminate from it the blight of partisan politics. There was a time when the people wanted parks and did not get them, because the politician saw no profit in them. But after they had been established, parks and recreation suddenly became of great political value because the "faithful" could be given jobs in them.

170

Continued dependence upon Federal and even state aid in the sense that the cost of park maintenance may be put upon the people's tax duplicate—whether Federal or state—will prove a boomerang. Such appropriations will be treated by the legislators either as charity or as a political investment. In neither case will parks live long or lead a useful, happy, and successful life. Parks are not eleemosynary institutions. Park visitors are citizens who pridefully consider themselves stockholders in a growing concern, not suppliants of charity or political favor.

During the years of its existence, Yellowstone National Park has served as the park movement's outdoor laboratory. For eighteen years it remained the only national park in the world, and it was and ever has been the first proving ground of park philosophy. Because it has largely influenced policy and practices in the parks which followed, it may well be chosen to illustrate progression of park ideals as well as of practical administration.

In 1932, Louis C. Cramton, a Representative from Michigan and a staunch supporter of parks, summarized the first twenty-five years of Yellowstone's history, emphasizing the evolution of current policies. The following extract of his presentation is taken from "Recreational Use of Land in the United States" by The National Park Service (1938).

During that period of time, there was fought out in the Congress of the United States and gradually crystallized in the Nation that fairly definite code of policies which now obtains in the administration of the national parks and monuments. . . . The history of the first quarter century of Yellowstone National Park is, in fact, the history of the development of our present national park policies.

Some of these policies are so universally concurred in that it does not occur to us now that they ever could have been questioned.

Others, not so universally accepted, have become thoroughly established as our national policy . . . through the trials of Yellowstone. Among these policies may be noted the following:

1) That the Federal Government may, under proper circumstances, itself undertake the administration of a reservation of land "dedicated and set apart as a public park or pleasuring ground for the benefit and enjoyment of the people."

It is true that in 1872 this region was a part of the public domain of the United States within certain of its territories, and, therefore, the question of turning it over to a State for administration was not at that time directly an issue. That course had been followed a few years previously in the case of Yosemite, and the brief debate in the Senate, January 30, 1872, in connection with the passage of the Yellowstone bill shows that the experiment of turning great scenic regions over to the state for administration was not deemed successful. The merit of Yellowstone as a park project and its outstanding importance did much to establish a general policy of Federal control in such cases. After the territories concerned became States, demand for transfer of control to the States could, as in Yellowstone, make no headway.

2) The twin purposes of such a reservation are the enjoyment and use of the present, with preservation unspoiled for the future. The act of March 1, 1872, set the area apart as a "pleasuring ground for the benefit and enjoyment of the people," and at the same time required "the preservation from injury or spoliation of all timber, mineral deposits, natural curiosities or wonders, within said park and their retention in their natural condition." There has never been any serious controversy in Congress concerning the wisdom of each of these.

3) The parks are to be administered primarily for the enjoyment of the people. The early and long-continued contest concerning leases and concessions in the park has always revolved around the determination of Congress that the welfare of the visitor shall be the first consideration in park administration.

4) Enjoyment of these areas shall be free to the people. The preface to Dunraven's *Great Divide* voices protest against the fee

172

system, universal in Europe, which was securing widespread foothold in the United States, and popular appreciation of a non-fee system in the national parks.

The park came into being within a few years after the close of the Civil War when the national debt was large, taxation was onerous, and economy in Federal expenditures was necessary. Very soon came panic and years of depression. But at no time was there any proposal of a fee system in Yellowstone. All the debate stressed the idea that this wondrous land be free to the public. At first there was the theory that revenues from leases of needed utilities would be sufficient for the development and maintenance of the park. But as it became clear that this would not be the case and the needs became understood, the policy of appropriations from the Federal treasury began, 1878, and has never been seriously challenged.

5) Administrative responsibility shall be civil rather than military. The act of March 1, 1872 provides, "Said public park shall be under the exclusive control of the Secretary of the Interior."

With negligible appropriations and resulting lack of administration, attended by alarming reports of game destruction and park spoliation, Congress in 1883 directed the Secretary of War, upon the request of the Secretary of the Interior, to make necessary details of troops for park protection. It was also provided that the construction of roads should be under the supervision of an engineer officer detailed by the Secretary of War.

In 1886 the appropriation for the park carried the provision that thereafter a company of cavalry should be stationed there for the protection of the park and eliminated any appropriation for civilian administration. Complete transfer of the administration to the War Department was proposed in bills introduced and in Congressional debates. Because of the presence of troops on the frontier and the need for economy in Federal expenditures, this same military administration continued for some years, but at no time did the complete transfer of the administration to the War Department make any headway in Congress. Eventually Congress eliminated the military protection and became definitely committed to civilian administration and civilian protection.

6) The welfare of the public and the best interests of the park visitors are conserved by protective permits for needed utilities. In the early days there was much to fear, probably well-founded, that some monopoly would secure leases of land at strategic points which would enable them [the monopolists] to hold up the public. No feature of park administration has had the same amount of debate in Congress that there has been about Yellowstone leases. Through the insistence of Congress that the welfare of the visitor be the first consideration and through gradual growth of understanding of the necessities of the situation, the policy of protective permits with Government control of rates, service, and the extent and character of improvements has been developed.

7) The park area is to constitute a game preserve and not a hunting reservation. When the bill was under consideration in the Senate, it being observed that the destruction of game and fish for gain or profit was forbidden, Senator Anthony urged that "Sportsmen going there with their guns" were not wanted, that the park ought not to be used as a preserve for sporting. Senator Tipton urged a prohibition against their destruction for any purpose. They were satisfied with assurance that hunting would not be permitted, and that policy has remained unquestioned.

8) No commercial enterprise in a park is to be permitted except so far as is essential to the care and comfort of the park visitors.

9) The national interest shall be supreme in the park area, and encroachments for local benefit shall not be permitted. The fight to maintain and establish this policy in Yellowstone was spectacular, with well-financed and influential private interests, supported by some official sanction, determined to secure a right-of-way in the park area for a railroad connection, ostensibly for mining development, but actually, in considerable degree at least, for speculative purposes. Failing to secure such a right-of-way, the effect was made to eliminate from the park the area involved, in return adding to the park much larger areas desired elsewhere.

For years the House was amenable to the desires of the private interests, and the Senate was the stronghold of opposition under the leadership of Senator Vest. It is interesting to note how in this critical period so many men of the greatest caliber in the Senate rallied to defense of the public interests. And, when the Senate lost hope and was prepared to accept the inevitable, the House reversed its attitude. Finally the time came when any railroad right-of-way proposal or park segregation scheme brought definite adverse report from congressional committees. The disintegration of national park areas to meet local demands has been made impossible through the struggles that revolved around the Yellowstone.

10) Recreation is an essential purpose of park use even though secondary and incidental.

The Yellowstone Act sets the area aside as a "pleasuring ground for the benefit and enjoyment of the people." Senator Pomeroy, in urging the bill in the Senate, said, January 23, 1872, that it was proposed to "consecrate and set apart this great place of national resort, as it may be in the future, for the purposes of public enjoyment." The park then being five hundred miles from any railroad and its nearest railroad point so remote from centers of population under existing modes of travel, it is surprising that any large park travel could have been at that time anticipated.

The Montana legislature, in its memorial in 1872, asked that this area "be dedicated to public use, resort and recreation." The Hallet Phillips report, which had much influence with Congress in 1886, said the first object accomplished by Congress in the establishment of the park "was a pleasuring ground for the benefit and enjoyment of the people." Preservation of these areas for scientific study, or for the enjoyment of the aesthetic taste in looking upon the beauties of nature, or the preservation of the great species of game from extermination, or for the protection of an important watershed, are all purposes that have had congressional support. But the simple idea of the common people going to these regions and enjoying themselves—recreation—has always had strong appeal to Congress.

12) In the national parks nature is to be preserved and protected and not improved. The act of March 1, 1872, requires "retention in their natural condition." The report of the sub-committee of the committee on appropriations by Representative Holman in 1886 reads: "The park should as far as possible be spared the vandalism

of improvement. Its great and only charms are in the display of the wonderful sources of nature, the ever varying beauty of the rugged landscape, and the sublimity of the scenery. Art cannot embellish these."

The above are the principal policies of a legislative character, or affected by legislative influences, which now govern our park system. There is little doubt that many of our present policies and practices of a more administrative character were likewise evolved through experience in Yellowstone.

What we have noted in the broad field of conservation holds equally good in our park service, that is, the crying need for the modernization of our laws and regulations, instead of the forcing of compromises by way of more or less honest and effective patchwork as an attempted readjustment of the system.

Contemptuous reference to "horse-and-buggy days" is often neither kind nor just. But in the business management of our park scenic values we have a conspicuously flagrant case of legally enforced archaism—rule by the dead hand of the law, supplemented from time to time by incredible but inescapable bungle through palliating regulations and Congressional provisions.

At the time of its establishment, Yellowstone was five hundred miles from the nearest railroad. It didn't remain like that. It couldn't. First one railroad came to its borders, then another, until there were three. Automobiles followed. Reluctantly, for no provision had been made for them, automobiles were finally admitted in 1915. A revolutionary change began, with endless controversies over highways, cuts, fills, and so forth.

Yet the old demand, "to spare the park the vandalism of improvement," insistently prevails.

During the 1941 park season of less than one hundred days, the number of visitors in Yellowstone and Grand Teton reached a total of 630,815 persons. Similar and ever increasing numbers were reported from other public areas.

When the National Conference on State Parks was organized at Des Moines, Iowa, in 1921, it was hoped that a partial remedy for park overcrowding would result from its work. Although the direct aim of its membership of public-spirited men and women was the preservation of their own state's scenery in state parks—thus not only increasing the number of such areas so preserved, but also relieving some of the pressure on the National Park Service for the taking over of lesser areas of distinct scenic beauty—it was hoped that, by this potential spreading of the load, a concomitant lessening of tourist pressure throughout the entire park system would result.

Instead, the pressure became greater all around, on both old and new state and national parks.

Today we realize that, in order to cope with such new and unforeseen conditions, we must have a rejuvenation of our park rule. What was adequate in "horse-and-buggy days" will no longer do.

This overcrowding will upset Nature's balances more and more. It may have another undesirable effect. The bringing together of hundreds of thousands of people, in a comparatively small space and for a short season, might easily leave in its wake the same conditions that prevail in places of permanent conflux of dense population—the industrial city.

In other words, in order to take care of the mass of people who rush into the parks, water, food, shelter and quarters, garbage reduction and sewage disposal must all be arranged for on a comparable scale. Failure to do this will turn certain sections of our great scenic parks into quasi slums— park slums.

When new properties, such as the glorious Olympic Mountain region and Kings Canyon, are taken over or a new state park established, we must resolve not to repeat present errors. The difficulty lies in making plans and forming a policy of administration that will avoid the first misstep, which leads in the direction of more and more compromises and pitfalls in future administration and management.

In new properties the service areas should be built on the outer edge, not within the boundaries, of the property. Highways should give way to simple park roads, not for use by private automobile. Traditional pack-train service should be encouraged, transportation to isolated camp centers furnished. From here guides would lead exploration parties into wild country that has had a chance to remain wild. Construction and management of the various service areas might be undertaken by voluntary associations under the control of the National Park Service, it being understood that any structure or non-structural improvement automatically becomes the property of the National Park Service.

A similar method for the better protection of scenery and wildlife could be adopted in the old properties. In Yellowstone, for instance, a vast new service area might be built west of the west entrance on the Madison River, to provide for the rushing mass of gas-buggy itinerants who need recuperation and recreation after the exhausting strain of sightseeing.

The states and the Federal government should not yield to the vast rushing army of vacationists; it should view them, not as masses who have to be satisfied in whatever reasonable or unreasonable thing they may demand, but rather, as they surely would wish to be considered, as eager, thoughtful, and kindly folk who want to come under the spell of majestic nature—instead of becoming, against their will, part of the forces of progressive destruction.

State departments might well co-operate with the National Park Service by telling their people that any provision to take care of possible peak loads will ultimately not only spoil their own enjoyment and appreciation but will, with certainty, ruin that which we all love and which we have sworn to preserve.

But to succeed we must find millions and millions of our people who, in better understanding of the great difficulties, will work along to protect the remaining scenic glory of our country.

The creation of our national parks was a high cultural achievement. Into their safekeeping has gone an unbelievable amount of hard work joyously performed. Their roll of honor contains the names of Presidents, Secretaries, directors, members of Congress, superintendents, park workers— whether rangers or academicians—all of whom have given their best to the ideal of protection coupled with intelligent use, the basis of conservation. All have given lavishly to the cause—some even their lives.

So much personal sacrifice and devotion has gone into the making of our parks that they themselves seem to reflect this spirit of consecration. Of all public possessions, the parks stand out as do certain beloved individuals. Each has its friends, protagonists, and—if need be—defenders. It is almost a human relationship.

For that reason, there are occasional family rows respecting the proper method of bringing up a young park or treating an old one. These broils, if stopped, would be sadly missed by all. They not only bear witness to the personal sense of possession but to the expressed ideas of great freedom in these places. It is good, this assertion of difference in opinions, even though it concerns itself with particulars and minutiae, missing as it does, at times, the all-important conservation principle of combined use and preservation.

CHAPTER XVII

THE TOURIST BUSINESS

EUROPE, with its older civilization, long ago realized and exploited the economic value of its scenery, to such an extent that whole countrysides and provinces appear, directly or indirectly, to have lived on the tourist business. Among the most obvious examples were the Alps, Italy, Egypt, the Riviera, the Rhine, Bavaria, Holland, Paris, London, the English countryside, and Scandinavia.

The automobile and its offspring, the modern highway, have done much to turn American tourists toward the beauties of their own land.

National parks and state parks are our significant national monuments. In a thousand years from now there will be little, if anything, left of the man-made monuments of our time. The face of the country itself will be so changed that no one could possibly reconstruct the America of today, were it not for these great natural monuments which wise use and sympathetic treatment have left in their glorious original condition.

Park work, whether national or state, is part of the greater scheme of conservation, and it is but natural that the care and protection of our American scenery is inherently of historic and social importance. What more natural than to stress from the beginning the theory that this wonderland should be free to the public—especially when it was confidently expected that leases and concessions would bring in enough income to care for necessary development and maintenance?

But this income has not come up to expectations. On the contrary, it is, and has been consistently insufficient to meet the costs of ordinary upkeep—let alone provide funds for expansion of service. This wholly untenable theory of free service still is as popular as it is illusory. For free service to the people in one way has to be paid for by these same people in another.

The weakest spot in the park's armor is its handling of concessions. No wonder that "no feature of park administration has had the amount of debate in Congress that there has been about Yellowstone leases." And yet it is this excessive Congressional control which stands in the way of a common-sense business management on the part of the Department of the Interior. Take the case of the money collected from automobile license fees. The Department authorized its use, among other needs, for the maintenance of roads. Legislation now provides "that these fees, and all other park revenues, be turned into the Treasury as miscellaneous receipts."

This provision is unjust and short-sighted because it prevents the various units from approaching a much needed degree of self-support, the only fair and truly democratic way of operating. But that is not the way it is done, for "in general," according to the report of the National Park Service, "it is the intention of Congress that the national parks should be available for public use, and it has not been expected that they should be self-supporting."

THE TOURIST BUSINESS

If any private enterprise dared to operate in the manner dictated by Congress to the National Park Service, a Congressional investigation and subsequent legal action would soon clean out its archaic practices. If any private enterprise, maintaining and operating an equipment to handle half a million or more guests per season, could not show complete self-support, the suspicion of incompetence at least would be most natural.

Under prevailing conditions, the Park Service is tied hand and foot and, in consequence, cannot render the service which it would be capable and ready to give, and to which the visitor is entitled.

The casual visitor is apt to see only the obvious in park service. He does not know of the intense labor of the superintendent, ranger, naturalist, engineer, or other members of the staff to maintain natural balance as far as it is in their power to do and still make possible a high degree of popular service. But these men know that every visitor unwittingly levies a heavy tax on natural life. The tourist and his family admire bears, buffaloes, and elk, and are proud that their government protects these magnificent creatures. But what only a few know is that this protection, under quasi-artificial biologic conditions, has increased the number of elk and buffalo beyond the existing food supply, while the bear has definitely put himself on public relief and acts accordingly.

The concessions bring ever increasing worries to the park administrator. Housing, transporting, and feeding multitudes of people—reaching in spots the half million mark—over a period of slightly more than three months, in the mountains far away from the base of supplies, is not like taking care of the same number twelve months in the year

in a settled community. In the parks, the peak load is all out
of proportion to existing equipment, and the necessary additional equipment would be too costly to be carried during the
seventy-per-cent-dormant period of the year.

The operation of private summer and winter resorts is
simple compared with that of a national park. When a private enterprise has reached capacity, it proudly informs its
clientele that no more space is available. Not so in the parks.
Though from a truly recreational angle there may already
be too many customers, the concessionaires seek more—no
matter what the effect on the landscape.

In their successful struggle to remain beneficiaries, the
concessionaires left the role of omnipotent benefactor to be
carried out by the Federal government through the National
Park Service, which, of course, would be best equipped to
satisfy the still prevailing demand "to spare the park the
vandalism of improvement" and yet make the necessary
improvements.

The present system of concessions—fair to neither party
—has long been a thorn in the flesh. Born in an era of
sweeping skirts, leg-o'-mutton sleeves, and horse-drawn
buses, when the automobile was not, and when circumspect
railroad companies made everybody at home in the parks,
themselves included, it is now definitely outmoded. As a
phase in the upbuilding of park properties at a period when
selective clienteles could be appealed to, it was in keeping
with the time. Today, when hotel life and park needs—like
everything else—have changed, it too requires changing.

The error was in permitting private capital to erect its
own buildings on public lands in the first place. The fact
that this practice has not been corrected long before this,

and that it still continues, constitutes a weakness in the functional setup and an irritating interference with proper park management. In this place due credit should be given to those park concessionaires who are, indeed, superior operators. The fault does not lie with them but in the system, which unwittingly is in conflict with all other park interests.

These manifold park interests, expressing as they do the widely extended park uses, were not thought of in the original plan. They came about largely after the organization of the National Park Service in 1916, as part of a plan to give adequate opportunity for more receptive enjoyment through a better knowledge and understanding of the environment. Nature guides, museums, lectures—inspirational or on subjects of related flora, fauna, geology, archaeology, and history—pamphlets, maps, and many other features are just a few of the supporting materials for park appreciation. In fact, this "pleasuring ground of the people" is beginning to deserve its name. There will be more, not less, demand on the part of the public for increased service, which means increased cost for needed personnel and equipment, with an increased strain on the landscape.

Modern business methods should be adopted in the administration of our parks both old and new. Congressional appropriations should continue, but these should be less specific as to use—one severe storm, one bad forest fire can alter the picture completely.

Parks should be made more self-supporting! This in itself is a comparatively simple matter of administrative regulation, but it can succeed only if the moneys received remain in the park fund, instead of going into the general treasury.

A fair appraisement of privately owned structures on public land should be made with a view to acquiring them; a fixed percentage—say ten per cent per annum—to constitute the sum of amortization. Aside from establishing sound business principles, this taking over of privately owned structures would be more advantageous in theory than in fact. Actually the Park Service would acquire a number of properties more gorgeous than serviceable—or even safe.

It is fortunate that no calamity has occurred in some of these properties, for it is no secret that from the standpoint of conflagration hazards some rank high. No public authority would now issue building permits for such architectural caprices, and, inasmuch as the Service is primarily responsible for the safety of its guests, the service should be in a position to make them safe or to liquidate them.

With the Congress, of course, the duty of control should rest. A reorientation, as proposed above, not only would facilitate this control, but would enable the park service, relieved from worse than useless checks and balances, to become a free-running engine of social service.

As an example of self-support in a state park, let us refer to the annual report of the Division of State Parks, Land, and Waters, of the Indiana Department of Conservation. From it we cull the following figures pertaining to one small park of 1,500 acres: Gate admissions for the fiscal year ending 1937 amounted to $20,363.10. This represents a charge of ten cents for every person over eight years of age. The amount received from the concessionaire was $11,350.30. With additional receipts from camping charges, the total park income was $32,766.90. As compared with the total administration and maintenance cost, this made the property

168-per-cent self-supporting. (Indicative of the continued growth of service is the fact that, by 1940, five four-unit cottages adding twenty rooms had been added, resulting in a fifteen-per-cent higher return from the concessions.) The total investment in buildings was $187,462.00 and in non-structural items $54,511.00. The park inn and cottages, 117 rooms in all, operate on the American plan, with a daily rate of from $2.75 to $3.75 and five per cent reduction for a weekly stay.

Under such a self-supporting scheme as this, the state, the concessionaire, and, above all, the park visitors are both satisfied and pleased—the visitor, because he gets excellent service for little cost; the concessionaire, because through intelligent devotion at all times to the interest of the state and the guests he has built up a profitable business; and, lastly, the state, because the principle of self-support has made extension of the park system possible, and has permitted constant improvement of service in the various units.

The income derived from the operation of this and all other parks in this system is held in a revolving fund, available for use in operating and improving the park properties as the park administrators may decide is advisable. Income received from sand, gravel, and coal royalties from state-owned land is held and expended in the same manner.

Compared with the vastly greater scope of the national properties, the above figures are unimportant in themselves; their importance lies in the significant fact that, just as old-time country-store methods are not in vogue in the modern department store because they don't succeed, neither should they be perpetuated in public enterprises. And no one knows this better than those charged with the responsibility of management.

While state parks are nearly seventy-five years old, the greatest expansion has occurred within the last few years. In the last four years alone, an increase of eighty per cent— 600,000 acres—has taken place in state park holdings.

Because of this extraordinary extension, it has been obvious for some time that the state park craft is in for some rough and stormy sailing. State after state, driven to the need for park service curtailment because of scanty appropriations, is facing the problem of retaining scenic and recreational value areas and eliminating those which might be termed temporary relief projects, with their white-elephant structural and non-structural improvements, obtained through Federal assistance.

It is fortunate that so far the excellent corps of technicians and scientists of the Branch of Recreational Planning and State Co-operation was able to direct or at least assist in state park work. Without it, the states needing this talent, not being able to pay for it, would be helpless.

How much of the ambitious state park program will live depends chiefly upon three items: proper selection in the first place; careful planning of essential facilities; and businesslike administration.

To start a park, either public or private funds must be expended. That has been done in full measure. Funds not only for acquisition of land but also for plans and projects. From now on the entity will have to demonstrate whether it is an asset or a liability, a success or a failure.

So much for the general principle. In actual experience it will be found that some of these infants will not do as well as others. Some will have to be supported longer than others, just as some of our children have to be helped along after others have attained stature and independence. But, while we love them equally, we would be bankrupt if the majority were to remain dependent on us for life.

As an example, let us look at some figures out of the experience of the state park system of Indiana, not because it is superior to others, but because I know it best.

Parks came into being in Indiana in 1916. By 1922 there were four parks—Turkey Run fairly well developed; the other three just emerging from the chrysalis. Two of these, McCormick's Creek and Clifty Falls, have fully developed. The third, Muscatatuck, from an investment and service standpoint, has proven a mild failure because it was too small an acreage. This park was not selected by us but, unfortunately, wished upon us. These four parks, with Turkey Run far in the lead, had a total income of $10,855.40 in 1922.

Compared with this, the report for 1940 shows park earnings of $207,119.32 for a total of eleven parks. Of these, three are more than self-supporting—Spring Mill, 158 per cent; Dunes, 157 per cent; Turkey Run, 155 per cent. (The comparative recession of percentage in Turkey Run for 1940 is explained by a four-month complete shutdown of the park inn for improvements, installation of machinery, and general renovation.)

The average at this time for all parks in Indiana is 105-per-cent self-support.

The memorials, returning $3,704.65, are 51-per-cent self-supporting, which, in the nature of things, is a good showing. The total of all properties is 103 per cent, which, after deduction of cost for office and technical administration, leaves 77 per cent of self-support. It is confidently expected that within a few years the system will be entirely self-supporting.

There are many things we wish now could have been handled differently. It is not easy, on the other hand, to realize the many difficult problems involved when the sudden change in national transportation brought masses of people into these public properties.

The existing confusion arises, in part, from the loose employment of the two words *parks* and *recreation*. At all times it should be remembered that the two represent different values. Parks offer recreation of one kind; recreational centers that of another. Parks cannot be created on order. They represent the finest of scenery and are set apart so that their natural features plus fauna and flora may be preserved in perpetuity. Recreational centers, on the other hand, may and should be built wherever needed. Recreational use, compatible with the primary object of the parks, is desirable. Beyond that, city parks, county parks, and other recreational systems should be responsible for meeting the short-time, short-distance, out-of-doors demand through organized recreation for masses of people in their immediate vicinity.

The industrial centers with their abnormal concentrations of population owe a duty to their people to finance recreational areas within the bounds of accessibility.

All over the country we need many more purely recreational facilities than we now have, especially in close proximity to our underplanned and overbuilt cities. But these would be recreational centers, not state parks. No one in his right mind would advocate building a playground or even a social center fifty to a hundred miles away, unless he is an annihilator of space and heedless of transportation cost. Why then disregard the limited mobility of the populace and cram into parks, far beyond their rational capacity, all kinds of inappropriate forms of recreation which through disuse may soon be classed as waste—that is, perfectly good recreational material in the wrong place. If this tendency is persisted in, the inevitable result will be a crushing defeat for sane and effective advance in public recreation, on the one hand, and ruination of scenery and wildlife on the other.

Park administrators should have the courage to say "no" when more and more service with inescapable addition of artificialities is demanded. Frequently we have taken ill-advised steps simply because we saw no avenue of escape. That happens every time, as the sapient Mr. Dooley used to observe, "Whin we take the second shtep without having considered the furst one." With the current great expansion of recreational facilities, not enough care was taken to separate the distinctive qualities of parks, and park authorities have only too often overexpanded their recreational services instead of primarily maintaining the sanctity of their perfect natural entity.

When we look back twenty-five years and see how the older park builders had to grope and feel their way in the preparation of an area, the surprise is that more mistakes were not made. There was one saving grace—these men did not have enough money to make big mistakes. To the Branch of Recreational Planning and State Co-operation of the National Park Service, and its corps of competent scientists and technicians, the highest praise is that they have done so

well, notwithstanding the vast amounts at their command
and the outside pressure constantly exerted to spend them.
Their restraint indicates the superior quality of the technical and scientific staff.

Could the situation be improved? Of course it could. But
it can more easily be depreciated.

The building, planning, and maintenance of all parks is
so completely bound up with the public weal that we should
eliminate from it the blight of partisan politics. It has been
said that democracy is the luxury of a rich nation, but we
are not so rich that, in the wasteful turnover of politics, we
can afford to sacrifice knowledge and experience and bog
down once more to hit-or-miss practices of the rule of thumb.
Nor, if we persist in this extravagant and foolish method,
have we any right to speak of it as popular government.
That sort of thing is not popular and has never been popular. The people are helpless simply because their opinions
and wishes have not been followed.

Loria, the Italian economist [so Frederick Jackson Turner tells
us in his *American Frontier*], has urged the study of American
colonial life as an aid in understanding the stages of European
development, affirming that colonial settlement is for economic science what the mountain is for geology, in bringing to light primitive
stratifications. "America," he says, "has the key to the historical
enigma which Europe has sought for centuries in vain, and the land
which has no history reveals luminously the course of universal
history." There is much truth in this. The United States lies like a
huge page in the history of society. Line by line as we read this
continental page from West to East, we find the record of social
evolution.

Some time ago the attention of the national government
was called to a rare opportunity for visual education in the

192

reconstruction and operation of a complete colonial farm in the North, as the symbol of an era in our history, which politically and socially was the culmination of the ideas of the eighteenth century, in addition to being, in itself, the closing chapter of an economic period. Similarly, in the South, a complete plantation should be maintained. We also need a cotton museum. And, of all people, we have no history of the fur trade assembled in one building. This can still be arranged, and by all means should be. Those of us who have watched the "dying West" are hopeful, too, of seeing the fascinating history of the cattle-and-meat industry so presented.

Salt, too, played such an important part in our nation's founding that it should be possible to locate some of the salt springs, mark them, and point them out as a living lesson in American history. Turner reminds us that "the early settlers were tied to the coast by the need of salt, without which they could not preserve their meats or live in comfort." This need, then, was in part the cause for the search and consequent discovery of salt springs along the Kanawha, the Holston, and the Kentucky and in central New York; it was the finding of these which enabled settlers to cross the mountains.

Because of our mania for building reservoirs—called lakes—it will not be more than fifty or a hundred years before our streams will have been so perfectly regulated that they will no longer bear any resemblance to their natural meandering condition. Would it not be better if we would pick up, here and there, a lovely stream, still in its delightful native unpretentiousness, and see to it that for the benefit of posterity it remain undisturbed and unimproved?

If we once fully understand our own origin and development, if it becomes clear to us that it was not alone our European inheritances and traditions, but rather—and increasingly so as we expanded westward—the American factors of life which shaped our national destiny, we shall in turn take deeper pride as well as keener delight in things truly American.

Like mighty altars of the Master stand our parks—masterpieces of creation and the crowning glory of our land; rich storehouses of memories and reveries; guides and counsels to the weary and faltering in spirit; bearers of wonderful tales to him who will listen; a solace to the aged and an inspiration to the young. Let us so keep them as a sacred inheritance, and so transmit them to future generations.

To use and preserve—that is the story of all conservation. In our great parks, its "show windows," we have an unparalleled opportunity to display it to best advantage, and to spread its gospel to the other branches of our natural resources vital to our national life and security.

CHAPTER XVIII

THE CARE AND FEEDING OF PARKS

THE creation, maintenance, and preservation of a state park is a subject so close to my heart that, at the risk of repetition of ideas already expressed in the foregoing chapters, I should like to recapitulate here the experience of many years devoted to conservation work.

Preservation of Property

According to my concept of what constitutes a state park, the word "development" must be shunned. There is, however, a word of importance and significance to the conservator, and that is "preservation."

The word "development" connotes a man-designed attempt on the improvement of nature's handiwork, if the term is used in connection with a conservation project. Such an accomplishment being wholly impossible, you may, therefore, understand why the philosophy and creed of conservation abhors artificiality or the mechanical in the making of a state park.

Of course, we should have a bit of modern comfort, but in a state park we should confine this to a small portion of the park project and include it in the "service area." Even here, we must not encourage commercialism, and must build and operate our inns and conveniences only for the modest com-

195

fort of our park visitors, remembering at all times that the purpose of a state park, as we have defined it, is to keep intact for all generations to come a part of nature's original domain.

The organization of a state park area for the use of visitors is entirely subservient to the above definition. It is immediately evident that there must be some compromise between the basic policy and the necessity of handling crowds in such an area.

The first consideration is that of circulation. Visitors must find it convenient to get to and into the park, and, once they are there, the many points of interest must be made accessible. It should be the policy in state parks to build only such automobile roads as are essential and have a definite objective. Roads built with the idea that the park must be seen from an automobile are of tremendous cost, cause much mutilation of scenic beauty, and really do not serve as the best means of seeing the area. We find that, having landed the visitor in the park proper, the best transportation medium from then on is by foot, over trails that are easily and cheaply constructed, do not mar the scenery and furnish an ideal method of seeing a natural preserve. It is only on foot that one will take the time properly to appreciate the landscape.

Each park may have one or more service areas, the principal service area to be that provided for the parking of machines and for camping grounds, picnic grounds, shelter houses, bathhouses, and refectories. Usually there is some space in the park which will logically fall into this classification both by location and topography. The principal auto road will lead directly to this site and many foot trails will center at this point.

A secondary service area also essential is one to contain the inn and its attendant buildings. The policy in state parks should be to provide overnight facilities in the shape of state park inns or cabins, in the belief that these areas should be made available for vacation purposes. The keynote of these inns must be simplicity and wholesomeness. They should in no sense be luxurious resorts; the service should be limited, and the furniture throughout of the plainest and entirely informal. The inns should be built with the idea in mind of furnishing comfortable sleeping rooms and simple, well-cooked food at the lowest possible cost, so that they may be available to practically anyone. There need be no menu in the dining room, but instead what may popularly be called the "family dinner."

The majority of the produce may preferably either be raised in the hotel garden or obtained from the surrounding country. Every precaution must be taken to have well-cooked food, and the kitchens should be held to a high degree of sanitation.

Keeping in mind that state parks are undoubtedly a permanent institution and will be in existence for many years to come, it is apparent that no construction other than that which is permanent is advisable. The state park inns are then planned for simplicity of service, with ruggedness in construction, and with the view that they shall fit into the landscape in so far as possible.

In practically every locality where a state park is found, there is some prevailing early type of architecture which may be adhered to. Where this is not true, a type that easily adapts itself to the environment should be found. Wherever possible, native materials, such as stone and timber, should be used. As an example, shelter houses are usually constructed of posts of rough-hewn or sawn timber which support a roof covered with wood shingles. The entire structure may be treated with creosote stain to produce a neutral tone. It is simple, straightforward, and serves its purpose admirably. With a background of trees it is surprisingly inconspicuous.

The state park inns must be let to carefully chosen concessionaires, on a rental basis for the space actually used by them of about eight to ten per cent of the capital outlay. The leases should provide that the department shall have complete control of the prices to be charged. They should also reserve the right to corrective criticism of the service when it is inadequate.

It is apparent that the principle of letting concessions to the highest bidder is unsatisfactory. The experience of letting concessions in city parks to high bidders has been sad. The bidder often pays more for his concession than it is really worth, and the public is bound to suffer, for the concessionaire resorts to gouging both in prices and in service.

The service area is the logical field of the park concessionaire. The purpose of the concession, so far as it concerns the state, is the satisfactory rendering of a needed service to those who want it and pay for it, without additional expense to the taxpayer.

The experience in Indiana proved that the licensing of conditional concessions is the practical method of solving the special-accommodation problem.

Of course, the state enters into the granting of concessions with great care and some concern. The terms of the license are and should be such as to permit the state authority to regulate the accommodations and the prices, but the personal ambition and initiative of the concessionaire should be encouraged ever to raise the standard of this type of service. The key to successful concession operation is in the selection of the right person. The field is limited; the type of contract —safeguarding, as it must, the interest of the state government and the visitors—makes it generally impossible to interest the professional hotel-keeper and refreshment-stand operator. Naturally, the cautious public official will guard against subjecting himself to possible criticism on the grounds of playing favoritism or being charged with lack of prudence in the awarding of these contracts; he will, therefore, insist that the terms comply with all state government regulations and legal restrictions.

Clearly the park authority should grant an exclusive concession, precluding the possibility of cut-throat competition or divided profits, so that he can assure the concessionaire of volume business to compensate for the regulated price. It is obvious, also, that the state should see to it that the concessionaire is enabled to make a fair profit.

Too much attention can never be paid to this all-important functionary. The best-laid plans of park authorities and enthusiasts gang aft a-gley for lack of a capable concessionaire. It is he who has the double function, before he can consider his own pecuniary interest, of representing the park authorities as well as the touring citizen. If he does not have this complete understanding of what the state can give and what the visitor is entitled to receive, he will have no further opportunity to consider his own material interests, for there will not be any left. But in the measure in which he is capable of acting as the state's representative, playing with ease the part of mine host, he will find a rich reward and all kinds of opportunities to profit in a material way, as he should.

Outdoor recreation in this country has just begun to assert itself. From now on we shall see a great deal more traveling and visiting than ever before.

Popular appreciation of American scenery and history is of but recent origin. Development of proper facilities for bringing scenery and history within reach of the folks the country over is hardly keeping up with demand. Again, we have barely scratched the surface.

Europe long ago taught us that the tourist business can be made a profitable industry. It will succeed, privately or publicly, if placed on a sound economic basis. The enterprise will fail if administrators depend exclusively upon appropriations, gifts, or public charity, so far as state-park properties are concerned, and they will hasten the inevitable debacle of the whole business by a refusal to have management keep step with time. The $8.00 to $15.00 per day American plan is not of our kingdom. Park authorities are and must be concerned with folk of moderate means and must serve them well. Nor is there any reason why that could not be done. The aim must be to keep down travel cost, raising at the same time the quality of service. Or to put it another way: "Give more service for less money." Be assured that it can be done, and, when it is done, the income to state, concessionaire, and also to private resort managers, notwithstanding the reduced cost to the tourist, will be as great as it is now or greater through the vast increase in volume. When that increase arrives—for it is on the way—would not any state wish that it had betimes put on a dime gate charge?

In order to handle, with comparative ease, a large number of people, a well-defined service area is needed as a place of congregation and redistribution. To it leads an unavoidable parkway. From it radiate trails through woods and by shores. It serves, so to speak, as a filter. But, above all, it saves the landscape from ruin. It leaves this protected for the nature lover, student, artist, dreamer, and other impractical but highly important people.

Responsibility of Visitor and Administrator

The visitor who uses a particular park and gets the immediate benefit from it should contribute toward the cost of its operation and preservation. State parks ought to be made as nearly self-supporting as possible, or else the cost will have to be charged to the general taxpayer.

It has always been true that those things which are furnished to us free of charge are ill-used, abused, and unappreciated. The State of Indiana committed itself to a policy of making each park pay all or most of its expenses. From May to November all visitors, except children under eight years of age, coming into the parks are charged ten cents. This charge is made only during the uninterrupted stay of the visitor, but he may come and go on errands out of the park without any further charge. It is made, in addition, for its psychological effect in inducing appreciation of the park on the visitor, as much as for its material aid in furnishing funds for maintenance.

Responsibility for the preservation of a primitive landscape is large. Since all the areas are heavily wooded, the great hazard is forest fires. Visitors must repeatedly be cautioned to be careful of cigar and cigarette butts, and the use of fires for cooking and campfires should be greatly restricted. Such fires should be permitted only in the picnic and camping areas. Regulations also should be enforced to prevent the picking of flowers, the mutilating of shrubs and trees, and the defacement of rocks, buildings, and signs.

The use of firearms should be prohibited. With these simple regulations, it will be found possible to keep all areas in excellent shape and to find them in better condition from year to year. However, there should be no unnecessary prohibitions or regulations. Each visitor should be encouraged to use the park in every way possible for his own benefit. It is apparent that organized sports, such as baseball, golf, and the like, should not be permitted, since this would require the destruction of large areas of natural landscape. Likewise, so-called amusement devices such as merry-go-rounds, derby racers, and the like should not be there. The natural sports, such as hiking, swimming, horseback riding, fishing, and nature study, on the other hand, should be encouraged.

The real problem of state-park management is the intelligent utilization of the areas for service to the public. In Indiana, where most state parks are of comparatively small acreage—1,200 or 2,500 acres—the situation becomes particularly acute. Any plan that is evolved for the use of the parks by the visitors must be subordinate to the policy governing their establishment and development, namely, the preservation of a portion of the state's original domain in its primitive condition, now and forever.

Classifying Visitors

Millions visit state parks each year—individuals, families, and parties. It is amazing how adaptable natural areas are to the demands of the many types and desires. The indoor man comes for the air and quiet; the athletically inclined for the sports; the nature student for the museum; the teacher and preacher for inspiration and knowledge; the mother for relaxation from the family grind, for here her flock may be turned loose; and the dweller in rural districts can here find the crowds with which he wishes to mingle.

The visitors to the state parks from the standpoint of provisions for their care fall naturally into four groups:

Day use. First is that group, forming the greatest percentage of attendance, who come for picnicking and an outing for the day. The greater number appear on Sunday, but there is a steady flow through the week from May to November. This sudden inflow may involve a considerable expense in driving wells, pumping water long distances, and maintaining a purification system, but a safe water supply must be provided. From the standpoint of state control, there must be no question as to the purity of the water. In case of rain, storms, or the like, there should be shelter houses under which a normal crowd may gather.

Park Inn Guests. The second classification, in point of numbers, consists of vacationists who desire to have food and shelter furnished them. For these, build state park inns, to which cabins may be added whenever necessary. Sleeping quarters with good beds, running water in the rooms, electric lights, small writing tables, a couple of chairs, rag rugs on the floor, and bathrooms and toilets conveniently near are desirable. The lobbies of inns should be large, because, contrary to the city hotels, in the evenings they form the meeting place of all the guests.

Campers. The third classification, in point of number, is made up of the campers who bring their own equipment, tents, bedding, utensils, and the like. This type of park visitor, formerly numerous, is slowly on the wane. Certain areas with water, sanitary conveniences, wood, outdoor stoves, and a source of supplies close by must be set apart for the campers' use.

Cabins. The fourth classification is the number of people who allegedly prefer to rent a small cabin for light housekeeping. We hear much these days of a recommendation for housekeeping cabins of simple construction. We believe this demand cannot come from expert park men but rather from well-meaning enthusiasts. In the Brown County State Park, Indiana, where such cabins were built, the arrangement so far as general service is concerned proved impractical. Little housekeeping use was made of the unit of twenty cabins surrounding the Abe Martin Lodge, because the people occupying them would not even bring their own linen and preferred eating at the Lodge. The cabins, therefore, have reverted to the form of a scattered park inn, the upkeep of which is found to be more costly than the regular park inn where all housekeeping is done under one roof.

How can state park service be extended to wider use? How can we let fresh air and sunshine into the soul and body of those who most wish for and need it and have so little means of gratifying that wish? How can it be done, away from dole or charity, in order to help them maintain their self-respect?

Make no mediocre plans. Above all, avoid the commonplace. Ordinarily it is not difficult to tell the good from the bad; it has successfully been demonstrated by libraries, galleries, museums, and concert organizations that popular taste may be elevated above the treacherous morass of mediocrity. In a like manner, it is the function of parks to elevate, not merely to satisfy.

Thanks to the far-sighted policy of the government—through the epochal C.C.C. labors—the state parks have been vastly extended.

So far the states have been in the receiving line. What has been given to them will not automatically maintain itself. Thought must be given and adequate provisions must now be made by the states to safeguard the investment (a) by much-needed initial appropriations, and (b) by the provision of income in order ultimately to make them self-supporting.

The National Park Service, through its Branch of Recreational Planning and State Co-operation, has built up and is perfecting a corps of park executives whose services will be at the call of the states awaiting them.

Summary

To a state developing a new state park system I submit the following list of "Dos and implied Don'ts," which form a brief but safe program for administration:

1. Provide a well-planned service area.
2. Provide a safe and ample water supply.
3. Check the quality of the water supply regularly in season by analysis.
4. Provide for sanitary sewage and garbage disposal.
5. Regulate the quality and cost of food stuffs and lodging.
6. Furnish fireplaces and free wood for cooking to campers and picnickers.

7. Stop vandalism in the picking and digging of flowers and ferns, and so forth. (Best accomplished by appeals to the public.)
8. Keep a close watch for fires.
9. Avoid all artificial "improvements" in the park proper.
10. Limit automobile drives to the barest needs.
11. Construct easy and pleasant paths through the woods and along the water's edge.
12. Maintain a service of nature-study guides.
13. Make a small charge for parking, camping, and other special privileges, to assure proper maintenance.
14. Collect a small admission charge.

Service areas. In connection with these rules, let us look at the setup of the service areas. One purpose of the service area is to maintain park property and to protect it against improper use, the other to serve the following visitors:

1. Campers.
2. Picnickers.
3. Inn or cabin guests.
4. Group camps, such as Boy and Girl Scouts, denominational camps, orphans, and other groups of communal service.
5. 4-H clubs, providing for agricultural youth.
6. University study groups.

Equipment and service should be provided to maintain:

1. Gate and driveway to main service area.
2. Automobile parking space and garages.
3. Park roads.
4. Network of trails, including bridle paths.

5. Nature-study guide service. Museum.
6. Park Inn.
7. Cabins and community center.
8. Custodian's dwelling and offices.
9. Help's quarters.
10. Workshops.
11. Stables for saddle horses.
12. Bathing beaches and swimming pools.
13. Life-saving corps.
14. Fire towers for fire protection.
15. Shelter houses.
16. Camp fireplaces.
17. Park benches and picnic tables.
18. Refreshment stands.
19. Sanitary water supply, wells, and waterworks.
20. Toilets.
21. Sewage disposal.

No, our parks and preserves are not mere picnicking places. They are rich storehouses of memories and reveries. They are a solace to the aged and an inspiration to the young. When the congestion of an increasing population in days to come has changed everything but these primitive places, our state parks will be one of the most priceless possessions of our people.

When that time comes, let us hope that we present park folk and our successors will have met and properly solved the problems of park management so that the generations of that day will be aware that our own was not without vision, but was filled with a true devotion to the welfare of our beloved country.

6. SOWING AND REAPING

CHAPTER XIX

CONSERVATION ON THE MARCH

THE great epic of America has not yet been written. But when that day dawns and the unexampled story of the conquest of a continent through daring, fortitude, and creative genius is told—a tale of hardships, colossal waste, bloodshed, cruelties, and hope deferred; but also of gigantic endeavor, almost superhuman perseverance, and high achievement—we shall gain a new comprehension of the native richness of our land and of the support our great natural resources were to the pioneer and the settler, as they are to us today in their remaining forms, and as they will be to those who follow, conservation prevailing.

From the sacred codfish of Massachusetts to the prolific salmon of the Columbia, through three thousand miles of primeval forest, through desert, over prairie and mountain and still more forests, the pioneer made his way. Fish, game, and fur-bearing animals sustained him. With him came his family, and out of the privations of these heroic groups, in which women played such a gallant part, rose modern America.

There was little need for conservation in those early days. The country was immense, the people few, the natural resources apparently inexhaustible.

Yet, in spite of all this plenty, there were some far-sighted citizens; for, as early as 1626, the Plymouth Colony passed a law regulating the sale of lumber outside the colony. In 1677, the exportation of game or of hides and skins was prohibited in Connecticut. William Penn's Fundamental Ordinance in 1681 stipulated that in clearing land one acre in five should be left for trees.

Conservation is a complex subject, wherein all parts touch each other and are so interconnected and full of ramifications that you could not remove one without immediately interfering with all the other related parts. All of this had long been understood by scientists and other earnest thinkers, but no popular action was taken concerning it in the early stages of the conservation movement. In fact, up to the beginning of this century, many of the important natural resources were considered inexhaustible and in need of no protection, according to popular view. Private greed and public apathy went on reducing our natural resources at an alarming rate.

The wide and almost limitless field of conservation inherently belongs to the academician. The thought of conservation started not with the user, let alone the despoiler, but rather from the scientist's workshop. As early as 1873, and again in 1890, for example, the American Association for the Advancement of Science made itself heard regarding the waste of our forest resources, and in 1897 the National Academy of Sciences followed with a detailed statement of its own. As a result of these three pronouncements, a national Forestry Bureau came into existence and the principle of national forests was established.

It was forest waste and its effect on water resources that gave rise to the Inland Waterways Commission appointed by President Theodore Roosevelt in 1907, to be followed by the "Meeting of Governors," at the White House in 1908, to study the ways and means of conservation in the various states. The closing words of this meeting's declaration of principles were: "Let us conserve the foundation of our prosperity."

Following the White House Conference of Governors, President Theodore Roosevelt appointed the National Conservation Commission, composed of forty-nine men, drawn in about even numbers from scientific work, politics, and industry.

The commission immediately went to work on a nation-wide survey of our national resources. Handicapped as usual by lack of funds, the commission nevertheless, by a presidential executive order, had the valuable assistance of the various government bureaus in their respective fields. By the end of the same year (1908) the report was finished and laid before the President. It was printed in three volumes as Senate Document No. 676 (1909) and is the first inventory made of the nation's resources.

Approximating facts and naturally incomplete in material, this report has nonetheless served admirably as the basis for scientific and technical appraisement.

One would think that of all important bodies the Congress would have been first to appreciate and to further the work of the President and the commission. Far from it. The Sixtieth Congress on the contrary did everything to balk, frustrate, and defeat their labors—first, by refusing a $25,000 working appropriation for the commission; second, by forbidding any assistance by the scientific bureaus; and, lastly, by refusing to provide a much-needed popular edition of the report.

The forces of reaction and heedlessness had momentarily triumphed, but they could not destroy the movement. Its leaders valiantly carried on as an unofficial body, calling themselves "The First Committee of Conservation"; subsequently, in the autumn of 1909, they formed the National Conservation Association. From that time stems the creation of state conservation departments all over the country. Yet those most deeply interested in the work, perhaps on account of their interest and understanding, were the first to sense the insufficiency, the inadequacy of their labors. By and large, notwithstanding excellent and therefore heartening progress, the movement as such remained in an academic stage.

Then, with President Franklin Delano Roosevelt's inauguration in 1933, came the advent of the "New Deal."

Scarcely had the President finished his inaugural address, and before his first day as Chief Executive was over, he had initiated the Civilian Conservation Corps as part of this new plan, by blocking out roughly with pencil and paper the skeleton of such an organization (see illustrations). On March 9, he outlined this plan to the Secretary of War, the Secretary of the Interior, the Secretary of Agriculture, the Director of the Budget, the Solicitor of the Department of the Interior, and the Judge Advocate General of the Army. He found them in enthusiastic agreement with his idea.

The Department of Labor was charged with the selection of the junior enrollees between the ages of eighteen and twenty-five in the continental United States. The Veterans Administration was empowered to select veterans, to whom enrollment was also open. The War Department was directed to handle the physical acceptance of the men selected for enrollment, their assignment and transportation, administration and discipline in the camps, sanitation, medical care and hospitalization, education, and welfare. The Departments of the Interior and of Agriculture were asked to give technical supervision to the work projects of the Corps. The Office of Education was placed in charge of the educational program, acting through the Army. The Army was also given technical supervision over a few of the work projects.

On March 21, 1933, the President asked Congress to pass legislation for the immediate creation of the C.C.C. The recovery measure, known as "An act for the relief of unemployment through the performance of useful public works and other purposes," included the necessary provision. Acting immediately upon this authority, Mr. Roosevelt issued an executive order on April 5, 1933, by which he appointed the late Robert Fechner as Director of Emergency Conservation Work, and provided for an advisory council representing the Secretary of War, the Secretary of the Interior, the Secretary of Agriculture, and the Secretary of Labor. Under this same order, he released $10,000,000 to finance the start of the program.

Mr. Fechner immediately set to work mobilizing the forces of the government placed at his disposal. The Department of Labor arranged for co-operation with relief and welfare agencies in each state and local community for the selection of enrollees. The War Department assigned regular and reserve officers to its end of the program. The Departments of the Interior and of Agriculture outlined work projects in parks, fields, and forests, and assigned technical personnel to the work.

On April 17, 1933, the first youth were enrolled in the C.C.C., and ten days later the first work camp was set up in George Washington National Forest, Virginia, under the technical supervision of the United States Forest Service of the Department of Agriculture. By early June, the quota of 250,000 junior enrollees, plus 25,000 local experienced men, 25,000 war veterans, Indians on reservations, and young men in the territorial possessions were settled in 1,468 forest and park camps of 200 men each, in every state of the Union.

After three months of operation, the C.C.C. received the full endorsement of the President as a working organization, and plans were made for a second enrollment to begin October 1, 1933. Widespread public approval was the most significant result of the first year's work of the Corps. In this period the C.C.C. had constructed 25,000 miles of truck trails in forests and parks, 15,000 miles of telephone lines for forest protection and area administration, 420,000 erosion check dams, and had carried out disease and insect control on 3,000,000 acres of forest lands, planted 98,000,000 seedlings, carried out forest stand improvement on a million acres, and put in 687,000 man-days on fire fighting.

The second year of the C.C.C. began with an enrollment of 300,000 men. The President increased this strength to 350,000 by an executive order on July, 1934, which provided for the inclusion of 50,000 men from drought areas in the Central States. By this time the C.C.C. was a smooth-working organization with its enrollees housed in wooden barracks instead of tents. The educational program, emphasizing training on the job and the elimination of illiteracy, was under way. The men were receiving good food, more comfortable clothing, had opportunity for education, recreation, and self-discipline, and were sending from $22 to $25 a month back home. Each enrollee had between $5 and $8 a month to spend in camp.

On the recommendation of President Roosevelt, Congress provided funds through the Emergency Relief Appropriation Act of 1935 for continuation of the C.C.C. until March 31, 1937. In April, 1935, the President authorized employment of as many as 600,000 in the Corps, and the maximum age limit was raised from 25 to 28. Subsequently the minimum limit was reduced from 18 to 17. Because of the improvement in business conditions with increasing opportunities for private employment, it was deemed inexpedient to enroll the full quota, and the enrollment objective became 500,000. The number of camps to be placed in operation, originally set at 2,916, was reduced to 2,652. On August 31, the enrolled strength was 505,782, an increase of 115 per cent over the April 10 strength of 235,732.

From that time, a gradual reduction of C.C.C. strength was worked out. On January 1, 1936, the personnel numbered 428,000 in 2,428 camps. By January 31, 1937, the authorized strength had been dropped to 350,000 and the number of camps to 1,991.

On June 28, 1937, Congress enacted a bill, which the President approved, by which the C.C.C. was set up as an independent agency, not allied with other agencies or activities treated in emergency relief legislation—and its life was extended for another three years.

Effective July 1, 1939, under Federal Reorganization Plan No. 2, the Civilian Conservation Corps became a part of the Federal Security Administration.

Following the death on December 31, 1939, of Mr. Fechner, who had served so ably as director of the Corps ever since its establishment, James J. McEntee, formerly the assistant director, was appointed by President Roosevelt to succeed Mr. Fechner as of March 5, 1940.

By the end of its seventh year, the C.C.C. had provided jobs for approximately 2,500,000 persons. In addition to its work for the conservation of resources, it has aided thousands of manufacturers, wholesalers, jobbers, retailers, and small businessmen. Up to March 31, 1941, the estimated obligations of the C.C.C. totaled $2,827,895,000, of which $1,-454,746,000 was expended for salaries and wages, and about $1,373,149,000 for supplies, materials, services, lands, equipment, and so forth. A very substantial portion of this money was expended locally, thus helping local businessmen. In the same period, the enrollees sent a total of $574,000,000 home to their dependent families.

More than 150 major types of work were carried on by the C.C.C. These may be classed under the general head of Forest Protection and Conservation, Recreational Developments, Soil Conservation, Aid to Grazing, Aid to Wildlife, Flood Control, Reclamation, Drainage, and Miscellaneous and Emergency Activities.

In its war against the greatest enemy of the forest—fire —the C.C.C. has built 3,880 fire towers and houses, and connected these lookout places with wardens, fire fighters, and forest officers by 77,930 miles of telephone lines. A total of 139,000 miles of roads, trails, and fire breaks have been built for further protection. The Corps has spent 5,600,000 man-days on forest-fire fighting. Control of insects and disease has been carried out over 19,500,000 acres.

CONSERVATION ON THE MARCH

A conspicuous contribution to forest resource building has been the tree-planting activities of the C.C.C. As a result of C.C.C. activities, the number of trees planted in national forest areas jumped from 25,000,000 in 1932 to more than 267,000,000 by the C.C.C. alone in the fiscal year of 1939. Altogether, approximately 1,800,000,000 trees were planted in the first seven years of the C.C.C.

From the standpoint of conservation in its fullest meaning, the C.C.C. has made one of its most noticeable contributions in the field of recreational developments. Numerous projects carried on for the protection, conservation, and development of national, state, county, and metropolitan parks have made these areas more accessible to the people who use them. In addition, many recreational developments have been carried on in national forests incidental to forest protection and maintenance work. These have included the clearing of hundreds of camp sites and the providing of fireplaces, water, and sanitation in every case.

In the national parks and monuments, and related Federal areas, the work of the C.C.C. has been aimed at the protection and conservation of the scenic, historic, archaeologic, or geologic resources of these areas, and their development for use in line with the policies of the National Park Service.

Funds and man power made suddenly available to the states and their civil divisions through the C.C.C. gave unprecedented impetus to the extension and development of state, county, and metropolitan park systems. States which had given little if any attention to developing park systems awakened quickly to the importance of recreation service as a function of government. Since 1933, state park acreage has been increased somewhat more than 100 per cent. At that time it totalled 965,057 acres, exclusive of the Adirondack and Catskill state forest preserves of 2,345,634 acres in New York. By June 30, 1939, the total was approximately 1,918,863 acres, exclusive of the Adirondack and Catskill preserves, showing an increase of 953,806 acres. Since 1933 there has been an increase of about 581 park areas in 45 states and these now number some 1,400 areas.

This was an ambitious undertaking and time only will tell how much of it may survive. Much will depend upon careful initial selection, followed by competent state park administration and practical business management, for from now on the states are strictly on their own.

So well was Federal and state co-operation for recreational developments demonstrated in the first three years of the C.C.C. that Congress, in 1936, passed the Park, Parkway, and Recreational Study Act under which the Secretary of the Interior was authorized to make, through the National Park Service, a comprehensive study of the park, parkway, and recreational area facilities and programs throughout the United States for the purpose of correlating these facilities and programs under a national plan. The Act further authorized, on a permanent basis, co-operation between the National Park Service and the states in planning recreational areas, systems, and programs.

On Federal and state lands, many historical sites have been restored and preserved, thus adding immeasurably to the cultural stores of the nation.

In national and state forests, recreational opportunities and facilities have also been tremendously increased by the work of the C.C.C. Under Forest Service supervision, the Corps has developed more than 3,500 camp grounds in the national forests, where simple facilities are provided for campers and picnickers; in addition, it has enlarged and improved many camp sites established earlier.

C.C.C. forces have also been used in the development of a new type of outdoor play area known as the recreational demonstration area. In twenty-four states in regions close to large centers of population, the Federal government has bought up land better suited to recreation than to any other use, and here the National Park Service is developing thirty-two vacation-type recreational demonstration areas.

Translating all the C.C.C. recreational accomplishments into terms of human welfare and happiness, we find that millions of our citizens who heretofore were unable to enjoy the physical, mental, and spiritual benefits of outdoor recreation because of the lack of sufficient parks and facilities are now able to do so. Thus the C.C.C. has contributed immeasurably to a program which has a highly important part in the conservation of the nation's valuable human wealth.

Since the establishment of the Soil Conservation Service, C.C.C. operations had been growing steadily in the field of soil-erosion control on farm lands; 28,894,960 acres in the work areas covered by C.C.C. camps were operating under the Soil Conservation Service.

Erosion-control work carried on by all types of C.C.C. camps has involved the building of more than 5,350,000 check dams and water-retention structures of various types, the planting of a half billion quick-growing trees for soil-fixation purposes, the sloping of hundreds of millions of square yards of gully banks, and the planting of slopes to grasses to check erosion.

The C.C.C. has aided wildlife directly by assisting the

Fish and Wildlife Service (formerly the Biological Survey) in expanding and developing its nation-wide system of wildlife refuges.

The most important C.C.C. work on flood control has been in Vermont, New York, and West Virginia, under the supervision of the Army Corps of Engineers. In the Wonooksi Valley, Vermont, three major dams have been built and a fourth is under construction. Since 1933, 6,085 impounding and diversion dams have been constructed.

Three general classes of work were done on reclamation under the supervision of the Bureau of Reclamation, Department of the Interior. The first of great importance in protecting the government's large investment in reclamation was rehabilitation of existing storage and irrigation systems; the second, development and construction of supplemental storage facilities for projects in areas seriously affected by the droughts of recent years; the third, construction of recreational facilities at irrigation reservoirs.

Some 84,400,000 acres of agricultural lands in the United States depend upon drainage. Work in this connection was confined to projects benefiting lands that are unquestionably of high agricultural value when properly drained. The improvement of drainage through clean-up of neglected ditches has saved crops and at the same time cut down the drainage-tax burden of residents of drainage districts. It is considered that the work done thus far has been worth millions of dollars to the communities affected. This work was supervised by the Soil Conservation Service.

An average of about 7,500 American Indians were enrolled in the C.C.C. They were engaged in various kinds of work for the conservation and protection of their own lands and homes on the reservations.

Enrollees have spent 1,810,000 man-days assisting in current emergencies. Widely distributed throughout the country and ready at an instant's notice to go to the aid of a stricken community, they have saved hundreds of lives and millions of dollars' worth of property through their prompt action in these situations.

Renewed self-respect and spirit on the part of the men constitute the most significant good that has come out of the C.C.C. Enrollees have gained an average of six pounds in weight the first two months they were in camp. Approximately 2,400,000 men have been in C.C.C. camps since 1933, including 2,209,000 young men, 141,000 war veterans, 60,000 Indians, and 30,000 territorials. Education and practical-work training have been given to more than 1,750,000 young men. More than 85,000 illiterates have been taught to read and write, and more than 500,000 enrollees have left the Corps to accept private jobs prior to completing their terms of enrollment. About 600,000 have been better grounded in elementary school subjects, and more than 400,000 have taken high-school courses.

It is difficult to make a final appraisal of the C.C.C.'s value. Attitudes toward it vary with varying political, social, and economic conceptions or preconceptions. Although created as an emergency measure, and in spite of its serious handicaps by way of a politically ordered administration, it has a record of genuine accomplishment. Nor should these gratifying and salutary results be weighed exclusively on the basis of material results. An appraisal of individual and, through it, communal gain, in itself imponderable, must be included if only by the symbol x. To the young workers accrued the profits of strengthening of mind and body. The training and teaching they received has given them courage and self-reliance. As a national school it has demonstrated its value as a sound investment.

Public opinion has justly endorsed the principle of the C.C.C. The people expected it to function as a conservation agency, protecting and conserving our natural resources, both material and human, for the good of all. That being so, it was mandatory that the C.C.C. set a national example— negatively, in the avoidance of waste; positively, by achieving results far in excess of its cost.

The weakest spot in the whole C.C.C. setup was its fiscal structure, which was transitory and almost evanescent. We must now ask ourselves what is to become of the huge financial investment of millions and millions of dollars under such conditions. Nine years of costly labor have built fortifications of peace in our parks, forests, and fields. Multitudes have enjoyed these manifold blessings. To underestimate this work or to abandon these havens to their fate would amount to an act of national sabotage. Such a brainless performance would not only wipe out a vast pecuniary investment, not only destroy the machinery from which flows social betterment, but would with certainty undermine national morale.

Thousands of youths who served in the Corps will long remember the products of their labors, for they looked upon the things that they built with the pride of personal achievement—perhaps the first one in their lives. Neglect of these works will not pass unnoticed by these responsible citizens of tomorrow.

CONSERVATION ON THE MARCH

The C.C.C. has stood for conservation. We have now reached a point where we must all do our best to conserve the efforts of the conservators.

The President from the beginning of his administration stressed conservation of our material and human resources. Of the many agencies created three have had a direct bearing on the actual processes of conservation as I have tried to present them. In effect these agencies have exerted a wide and wholesome influence on better understanding of conservation's needed machinery. They are the Public Works Administration, the C.C.C., and the National Resources Planning Board.

Dr. Charles E. Merriam has told us that "planning is an organized effort to utilize social intelligence in the determination of natural policies." That being the case, the earnest co-operation of all is needed. We have implicit trust in our representative form of government, but through our lack of more active participation we have placed an excess load of cost and waste on the government by tolerating disorder. Responsibility for good government rests with the individual citizen, and not responsibility for good citizens with the government. If we shun this responsibility and force the government to assume the whole load, whether county, city, state, or federal, remember that that which a government can do for us it ultimately will do to us.

The war has placed additional responsibilities on us, but battles are fought not only on land, sea, and in the air, not only by correlated battle lines and production lines, but by the devotion, determination, and consecration of a whole people.

Let us continue to strive for a better order in public affairs. Less waste and more saving. Down with corruption, chiseling, grafting, and cynical privilege. Let us be helpful, as we surely want to be, to our fellow citizens, and mindful of public and personal health, both in body and soul. Let us send sunshine into the hearts of those whose children are fighting in freedom's front lines.

Let us be of good cheer and stout faith that through courage, sacrifice, vision, and kindliness we shall make our contribution to the end that our country remain what it ever has been throughout its glorious past: a land of promise, of opportunity, of freedom, and of sunshine.

Today we stand at the crossroads where signs point to success or failure. On the road we choose depends the future well-being and prosperity of the nation. It will determine, in large measure, our way of life.

Our natural resources are the source of our health and our wealth, of our strength and our independence. They are important not merely to the conservator and the exploiter; they are essential to you—to every man and woman in America, and to the children who will inherit the land.

Which road are we to follow? It depends, in the final analysis, on you.

APPENDIX

CHRONOLOGY OF EVENTS AFFECTING CONSERVATION OF NATURAL RESOURCES

A chronology of events affecting the conservation of natural resources seems desirable for many reasons. Such a tabulation should attempt to include a consideration not of many but of all the sources of national wealth and should aim to show when, where, and by what agency the first step was taken which controlled or at least affected the use—wise or otherwise—of any given item in the wide field of those seemingly inexhaustible riches which the Governors' Conference at the White House, in 1908, recognized as the "source of our prosperity."

The present compilation of a chronology began simply enough as a by-product of reading and writing—a mass of material accumulated, a mélange of seemingly unrelated happenings which had to be assorted. Any student of the conservation movement can see for himself in the resultant product the utter lack of any but the most haphazard approach by the various state governments. Yet throughout it all, if viewed in its totality, there appears a general trend in the direction of needed national action.

It should be remembered in that connection that the states and not the Federal government advanced the idea of Federal control, of a policy of comprehensive treatment of our natural resources. This desire, less altruistic than practical, follows the troublesome experience that neither oil and minerals, nor surface and underground waters, nor plant pests and diseases, to mention only a few items in conservation, are amenable to artificial state boundaries.

So far as I know, this is the first attempt to recite, in the order of their occurrence, events touching the entire field of conservation;

it will disclose, I hope, the weight of economic pressure as well as the social and political apprehension which point to the need for a better national order in matters of use and preservation; but more-over—and this may be its only claim for possible merit—it may offer a corollary to the proved proposition that no single resource may be considered apart from any or from all others, by being in itself eloquent testimony as to why we need a United States Department of Conservation.

CHRONOLOGY OF EVENTS AFFECTING CONSERVATION OF NATURAL RESOURCES

1626—Plymouth Colony regulated the sale of lumber outside the colony; it was the first of many similar laws in New England.

1627—Joseph d'Allion, a French missionary, described oil as a product of the Mohawk Valley.

1629—Hunting and fishing privileges were granted to settlers in New Netherlands by the Dutch West Indies Company.

1631—The first sawmill in America was built at Berwick, Maine.

1677—Exportation of game or of hides and skins was prohibited in Connecticut.

1681—William Penn's Fundamental Ordinance stipulated that in clearing land one acre in five should be left for trees.

1687—New Hampshire enacted law to protect an important food supply by regulating mackerel fishing.

1691—Licenses were required in Virginia for hunting in areas remote from settled districts.

1691—Charter of Massachusetts reserved largest trees for the use of the Royal Navy.

1693—Closed season for deer in Massachusetts.

1704—The Maryland Legislature recognized that the public had rights in the matter of water power.

1708—In New York, heath hens, ruffed grouse, quail, and wild turkeys were protected in certain areas for a part of the year.

1717—Levee construction along the Mississippi was begun at New Orleans.

1730—Maryland was the first colony to pass a law to prevent hunting deer by firelight.

1738—Virginia passed an act for the protection of does.

1739—First deer wardens in America were appointed in Massachusetts.

1739—Massachusetts Bay Colony prohibited tree cutting on Cape Cod.

1744—Massachusetts Bay Colony authorized the establishment of a "common woods."

1750—Delaware prohibited Sunday hunting.

1762—Anthracite coal was discovered by Parshall Terry near the present

APPENDIX

site of Wilkes-Barre, Pennsylvania. About 1769 it was first successfully used as fuel by Obadiah Gore, a blacksmith of Wilkes-Barre. In 1793 first organized attempt to mine coal was made by the Lehigh Coal Mine Company about nine miles from Mauch Chunk, Pennsylvania.

1776—Continental Congress decreed a closed season on deer in all colonies but Georgia.

1781-1790—The public domain was created by the cession to the Federal government of the claims held by the states to lands between the Allegheny Mountains and the Mississippi River.

1786—Annapolis convention was called to settle contested water rights and urges assembly of a constitutional convention.

1787—Federal Constitution was framed in Philadelphia.

1787—First sales of public lands in the United States were conducted in New York.

1787—Land Ordinance provided for survey of the public domain and its division into townships six miles square, each township to be divided into thirty-six sections of 640 acres each; the land was to be offered at public sale in units of 640 acres at a minimum price of $1.00 per acre.

1787—Coal is reported to have been mined in the Triassic Basin near Richmond, Virginia.

1788—First law prohibiting hounding was passed in New York.

1791—New York provided protection for the woodcock.

1796—The minimum price of public land was raised to $2.00 per acre and a credit system of payment was introduced.

1799—A law was passed directing the President to spend not more than $200,000 "in the purchase of growing or other timber or of lands on which timber was growing suitable for the navy. . . ." In 1817 a law was passed authorizing selection of lands producing oak and cedar suitable for naval purposes. An Act of 1828 authorized the creation of the Santa Rosa Island Live Oak Reservation. In 1831 an Act was passed empowering the government to reserve timber on public and other lands that it deemed suitable for naval purposes.

1800—The smallest tract of public land offered for sale was reduced to 320 acres and the credit system was further extended.

1803—The Louisiana Purchase.

1812—General Land Office was established.

1818—Massachusetts forbade shooting of robins in the spring. Massachusetts also passed a law protecting snipe from March 1 to July 4.

1819—Purchase of Florida.

1820—New Jersey was the first state to protect rabbits.

1820—The credit system of public land purchases was abolished; the unit of sale was reduced to 80 acres; the minimum price was reduced to $1.25 per acre.

1821—Massachusetts law forbade shooting on salt marshes between March 1 and September 1.

1823—Natural gas was first used for fuel or light in Fredonia, New York.

1823—North Carolina was probably the first state to provide for a geological survey.

1824—The decision of the Supreme Court in Gibbons *vs.* Ogden gave Congress paramount control of navigation in navigable streams and made possible the construction of navigation dams.

1824—The first appropriation for channel improvement work on water ways was made.

1830—Closed season on moose was established in Maine.

1831—Santa Rosa Island Live Oak Reservation, the first venture in forest management (established 1828) under the Federal government, was abandoned.

1832—Hot Springs, Arkansas, region was reserved for future disposal by the United States.

1832—First Federal game law forbade capture of game by any persons other than Indians, except for subsistence in the Indian country.

1832—First law protecting wild fowl, by prohibiting night shooting on water or the use of big guns for killing wild fowl for sale, was enacted in Virginia.

1832—George Catlin, a passenger on the "Yellowstone," the first steamer to go up the Missouri River to the mouth of the Yellowstone River, proposed that a large tract of land in this region be preserved forever as a "Nation's Park."

1841—Squirrels were protected by a Pennsylvania law.

1841—The Pre-emption Act granted actual settlers pre-emption rights to tracts of not more than 160 acres.

1844—New York Association for the protection of game was organized.

1844—Last record of existence of wild turkeys in five counties of upstate New York.

1845—Last elk in New York state killed in Genesee Valley.

1845—Texas was annexed.

1846—Rhode Island created the first closed season on ducks.

1846—Oregon settlement.

1846—This year marked the beginning of the abandonment of the policy of reservation and lease of mineral lands as too costly; by 1866 the policy of sale applied for all mineral lands.

1846—Michigan declared that property in gold and silver mined in the state was vested in its people and in their sovereignty.

1848—Mexican cession.

1848—Massachusetts law protecting wild pigeon netters by imposing a fine of $10 and damages for frightening pigeons from nests.

1849—New York Act authorized county boards of supervisors to make ordinances for the protection of fish and game.

1849—Gold rush to California.

1849—The Department of the Interior was established.

1849—The Federal government began to transfer title of public swamp lands to the states.

1850—Connecticut and New Jersey passed the first laws in the United States for the protection of insectivorous birds.

APPENDIX

1850—First attempt to introduce the English sparrow was unsuccessfully made by Nicholas Pike.

1850—The first grant of public lands in aid of railroad construction was made to the Illinois Central Railroad.

1851—Wisconsin prohibited killing of the prairie chicken February 1 to August 1.

1852—Office of county moose warden was created in Maine.

1852—California passed first protective law applicable to elk and antelope.

1852—First successful attempt to introduce the English sparrow.

1853—Gadsden Purchase.

1856—Massachusetts provided for the preservation of its aquatic resources.

1856—The State of Tennessee purchased the "Hermitage," the home of Andrew Jackson.

1858 or 1859—Establishment of deer park near Ottawa, Illinois, by Judge J. D. Caton.

1859—First successful use of wood pulp for paper manufacture.

1859—In Pennsylvania, Drake Oil Well was successfully completed, marking the beginning of one of our greatest industries.

1859—The Ladies' Mount Vernon Association purchased Mount Vernon to preserve it as a memorial to George Washington.

1861—Nevada provided first protection to mountain sheep and mountain goat.

1862—New York passed the first law protecting the wild pigeon.

1862—The Homestead Act allowed actual settlers to enter 160 acres of land.

1862—The Department of Agriculture was established.

1864—New York was the first state to adopt a hunting license law.

1864—Idaho established first closed season on bison.

1864—Congress transfers Yosemite Valley and the Mariposa grove of big trees to California for a state park.

1866—Joseph S. Wilson, Commissioner of the General Land Office, petitioned Congress to afforest the Great Plains in part.

1866—Mineral Land Act provided that mineral lands of the public domain, except those containing coal, should be open to acquisition by conforming to established local customs.

1867—Purchase of Alaska.

1867—First efforts to preserve Niagara Falls from defacement were begun.

1867—Wisconsin orders a thorough survey of its forests.

1868—Last great pigeon nesting in New York.

1869—Indiana established a Department of Geology and Natural Resources.

1869—West Virginia passed the first law in the United States to protect *all* non-game birds.

1870—Washburn-Doane Expedition to the Yellowstone country; Cornelius Hedges, a member of the party, suggested Federal ownership of the wonderlands.

1870—In this year and 1872 the price of mineral lands was set at from $2.50 to $5.00 an acre.

1871—American Institute of Mining Engineers recommended study of coal conservation.

1871—United States Fish Commission was created.

1871—Office of game constable was created in New York.

1871—Congress abandoned policy of making grants of Federal lands to aid railroads.

1872—Natural gas was piped on a commercial scale for the first time.

1872—Yellowstone National Park was established, the first of the system of national parks and monuments.

1872—J. Sterling Morton instituted Arbor Day in Nebraska.

1872—The First Federal appropriation ($5,000) for payment of special agents for protection of timber on public lands was made.

1873—American Association for Advancement of Science memorialized Congress and the States to enact laws for conservation of forests.

1873—Coal Land Act provided for disposal of known coal lands for at least $10 to $20.

1873—New Jersey passed nonresident license legislation.

1873—Timber Culture Act provides for the grant of a quarter section of land to anyone planting and protecting 40 acres of timber for ten years.

1874—The American Association for Advancement of Science at Portland, Oregon, presented a memorial to Congress advocating public forests.

1875—American Forest Association is organized.

1876—Congress authorized the Department of Agriculture to appoint a forestry agent, and Dr. Franklin B. Hough was chosen.

1877—Carl Schurz, Secretary of the Interior, urges the establishment of Federal forest reservations.

1877—The Desert Land Act provided for sale at low prices of a section of land irrigated by a settler for three years.

1878—Division of Entomology was created in the Department of Agriculture.

1878—Iowa was the first state to fix a bag limit on game of any species.

1878—The first boards of fish and game commissioners were established in California.

1878—Timber and Stone Act provided that in certain states tracts of 160 acres of public land valuable chiefly for timber and stone might be sold at $2.50 an acre.

1878—Timber Cutting Act authorized citizens of certain states and territories to cut timber from mineral lands without charge.

1879—Large numbers of European quail were imported and distributed in northeastern states.

1879—Provision was made for classification of natural resources as a preliminary to their disposition.

1879—The United States Geological Survey was established.

1879—Pennsylvania regulated the method of plugging abandoned oil wells to prevent water from reaching oil-bearing sands.

1879—Congress created the Mississippi River Commission to carry out a program of flood control.

APPENDIX

1879—Powell's classic *Report on the Lands of the Arid Region of the United States,* with its program for proper utilization thereof, was published.

1881—Decision in Wagner *vs.* People enunciated the principle that the game belongs to the state.

1883—Pennsylvania withdrew protection from the English sparrow.

1883—American Ornithological Union was formed.

1883—Texas reserved to the state all the minerals in her public lands.

1883—The State of New York prohibited the further sale of state land within the Adirondacks.

1885—Niagara Reservation was created by the State of New York to preserve Niagara Falls.

1885—New York established a forestry department.

1885—Adirondack Preserve, first state forest, was established by the State of New York.

1885—American Ornithological Union framed a model state law for the protection of non-game birds; it was adopted by more than a dozen states by 1900.

1885—Biological Survey of the Department of Agriculture was started.

1885—Mackinac Island was transferred by the Federal government to the State of Michigan as a state park.

1885—The Ohio Archaeological and Historical Society was founded to protect the antiquities of the State.

1885—A Federal Act made fencing of the public domain illegal.

1885—President Cleveland ordered cattle taken off the Arapahoe-Cheyenne Reservation because of overgrazing the range.

1885-1887—Commissioner of the General Land Office, W. A. J. Sparks, was forced to resign because of militant efforts to enforce land laws.

1886—Dr. Bernard E. Fernow was selected as head of the Division of Forestry in the Department of Agriculture.

1886—New York was the first state to adopt the American Ornithologists Union "model law" for the protection of non-game birds.

1886—Natural gas was brought to Pittsburgh.

1887—The Lincoln Homestead, Springfield, Illinois, was set aside as a state monument.

1888—Major J. W. Powell's *Lands of the Arid Region* resulted in the organization of an irrigation division in the Bureau of Geological Survey.

1888—The Secretary of the Interior was authorized to withdraw from private entry reservoir sites and other areas necessary for irrigation.

1889—The Ladies' Hermitage Association was organized to protect the "Hermitage," which was conveyed to the body by the State of Tennessee.

1889—The Association for the Preservation of Virginia Antiquities is founded to protect and preserve old landmarks.

1889—Prehistoric ruins at Casa Grande were established as a national park by Presidential proclamation.

AMERICA'S NATURAL WEALTH

1889—The law allowing public land to be secured at private sale or by "private entry" was repealed.

1890—American Association for the Advancement of Science presents a second memorial to Congress on the need of conservation.

1890—Yosemite, Sequoia, and General Grant National Parks were created.

1890—Fort Ancient, Ohio, one of the greatest prehistoric defensive earthworks in the United States, was the first archaeological area established as a state park.

1890—A Federal Act provided that railroad land grants should be forfeited opposite their unconstructed roadbeds where the legal time limit for construction had been exceeded; 5,000,000 acres were recovered.

1891—The President was authorized to set aside forest reserves on the public domain.

1891—Yellowstone National Park Timberland Reserve, the first national forest, was set aside by President Harrison.

1891—First meeting of the National Irrigation Congress.

1891—The Pre-emption law was repealed as well as the law permitting public sales.

1892—Timber and Stone Act of 1878 was extended to all the public land states.

1893—An Indiana statute forbade removal of oil from the ground unless the accompanying gas was utilized.

1893—Valley Forge, Pennsylvania, scene of the encampment of Washington's Continental Army in the winter of 1777-1778, was made a state park.

1893—President Cleveland by proclamation established Cascade Range Forest Reserve and Ashland Forest Reserve in Oregon.

1896—Cary Act provided Federal aid to irrigation.

1895—Forestry department was established in Pennsylvania.

1895—Michigan and North Dakota were the first states to adopt licenses for both resident and nonresident hunters.

1895—The American Scenic and Historic Preservation Society was created in New York to administer areas of scenic or historic interest.

1895—The nucleus of the Palisades Interstate Park of New York and New Jersey, the first extensive state park, was created.

1896—The United States Supreme Court, in Geer vs. Connecticut, declared game the property of the state and sustained the right of the state to prohibit the export of game.

1896—Gold was discovered in the Yukon. In 1898 the Klondike gold rush reached its climax.

1896—New York Chamber of Commerce urged a conservation program.

1896—A committee of the Forestry Association induced the Secretary of the Interior to request the National Academy of Sciences to investigate and report on a national forest policy. The report advised the creation of forest reserves of more than 20,000,000 acres.

1897—Memorial of the National Academy of Sciences on natural resources was submitted to Congress.

234

APPENDIX

1897—Act preventing trespass on National Military Parks.

1897—In Colorado the Lost Park herd of buffalo, last wild buffaloes in the United States outside of Yellowstone National Park, was killed.

1897—Federal Act restricted the right to take timber from the Public Domain free of charge to settlers and others on farms and claims.

1897—President Cleveland establishes thirteen forest reserves in the western states.

1898—Gifford Pinchot was appointed head of the Division of Forestry in the Department of Agriculture.

1898—The Provisions of the Act restricting the amount of timber that could be taken from public domain was extended to Alaska.

1898—The First college of forestry in the United States was established at Cornell University; two years later the Yale School of Forestry was established.

1899—Act of March 3 prohibited construction of dams in navigable waters except by authorization of Congress.

1900—Lacey Act, the first Federal law regulating the importation of birds and animals and interstate traffic in game and requiring packages of game to be marked so as to show name of shipper and contents.

1900—The President was authorized to withdraw temporarily from settlement and sale of any public lands and to reserve minerals as government property.

1902—Congress appropriated $15,000 for the purchase of buffalo for Yellowstone Park.

1902—Federal law authorized the importation of eggs of game birds under permit of the Secretary of Agriculture.

1902—Reclamation Act was passed; the Bureau of Reclamation was established in the Department of the Interior.

1903—Congress appropriated $1,000 for transferring elk to the Sequoia National Park.

1903—Executive order of March 14 set aside Pelican Island, in Indian River, Florida, as the first national bird reservation.

1903—Three convictions by the Federal Court in California for perjury in connection with the Timber and Stone Act, the first of the kind in California in fifteen years.

1904—American Civic Association was founded.

1904—The Public Lands Commission reported that much range land was overgrazed.

1905—The National Association of Audubon Societies was formed.

1905—Forest reserves were transferred from the Interior to the Agriculture Department.

1905—Wichita Game Preserve, Oklahoma, was established.

1905—The Public Lands Commission recommended the repeal of many so-called conservation laws as definite evils and working contrary to purposes of conservation.

1906—Antiquities Act authorized the Secretary of the Interior to set aside as national monuments portions of the public domain notable for scientific or historic interest.

AMERICA'S NATURAL WEALTH

1906—Grand Canyon Game Preserve was created in Arizona.

1906—Federal Act protecting birds on bird reservations.

1906-1909—Large areas of coal, petroleum, natural gas, phosphate, and potash lands were withdrawn from entry.

1907—Pennsylvania established game refuges on state forest reserves.

1907—Pennsylvania prohibited use of automatic guns in hunting game.

1907—Fifty-seven new national forests were created, bringing the reserved acreage to about 150,000,000 acres.

1907—Inland Waterways Commission was appointed to study conservation problems as related to waterways.

1907—Illinois Agricultural Experiment Station began field work on the control of soil losses by erosion.

1908—White House Conference of Governors on conservation was called by President Theodore Roosevelt.

1908—Phosphate lands were withdrawn from private entry.

1908—Suit was begun for the forfeiture of the Oregon and California Railroad grant; it marked the first time Federal government had declared or sought forfeiture because of a breach of terms prescribing the manner of disposal of land.

1909—The Federal government discovered gigantic land frauds involving about $100,000,000.

1909—A large amount of oil and phosphate lands and numerous water power sites were withdrawn from entry.

1909—The National Conservation Commission submitted the first comprehensive inventory of natural resources.

1909—The National Conservation Association, a civic body, was organized with Gifford Pinchot as acting president. Served as President from 1910 until termination of Association in 1925.

1909—By executive order, the Mount Olympus National Monument was created as a refuge for elk.

1909—Maine, North Dakota, and Washington prohibited the use of silencers.

1910—Bureau of Mines was established.

1910—The Society for the Preservation of New England Antiquities was organized.

1910 (June 25)—Congress authorized the President, in his discretion, to withdraw from sale any of the public lands.

1911—Weeks Forestry Act provided for co-operation between the states and the Federal government in preservation activities.

1911—American Game Association was organized.

1911—State Conservation Department was organized in New York.

1911—An agreement was entered into by the United States, Great Britain, Japan, and Russia, whereby the taking of our seals in the North Pacific was prohibited except under limited conditions.

1911—A Federal Act provided for the purchase by the government of privately owned lands, approved by Bureau of Forestry, thus making possible national forests in the eastern half of the country.

APPENDIX

1911—The Enlarged Homestead Act permitting entry of 320-acre homesteads was passed to encourage settlement in semiarid regions.

1911—Appalachian Forest Reserve Act authorized purchase of forest lands in the White Mountains and the southern Appalachians.

1911—Annual appropriation for the Department of Agriculture provided for furnishing trees free to settlers in the Sixth Congressional District, Nebraska.

1913—Weeks-McLean Act asserted Federal jurisdiction over migratory birds.

1913—The Miami Conservacy District of Ohio was organized to protect the Great Miami River Valley from flood by constructing a series of five retarding dams.

1913—Authorized appropriation was made for the Department of Agriculture to establish the Northern Great Plains Field Station at Mandan, North Dakota, part of its activities to be "growing, distributing, and experimenting with trees suitable to that region."

1914—The last passenger pigeon died in Cincinnati Zoo.

1914—Congress authorized investigation of the problem of flood control.

1914—Congress enacted a coal-leasing law for Alaska.

1915—State Conservation Department was established in New Jersey.

1915—The Supreme Court declared forfeited 2,300,000 acres of Oregon and California Railroad Company land and enjoined company from disposing of land or resources thereon until Federal legislation for disposition of same was provided.

1916—National Park Service was created, with Stephen T. Mather as director.

1916—Pisgah National Forest was the first national forest formally created in the East.

1916—The Stock-Raising Homestead Act was passed, permitting entry of 640-acre homesteads.

1916—Beginning of distribution of trees in Great Plains area.

1917—The Missouri Agricultural Experiment Station began pioneer soil-erosion control and specific soil and water-loss measurements.

1917—The leasing system was applied to potash lands.

1918—Migratory Bird Treaty Act of 1918 provided protection for birds migrating between the United States and Canada.

1918—"Save the Redwoods" League was formed to preserve the big trees of California.

1919—State Conservation Department was established in Indiana.

1919—State Conservation Department was established in Massachusetts.

1919—The National Parks Association was created to work for the preservation of outstanding examples of natural wonderlands.

1920—Mineral Leasing Act established the general principle of leasing mineral lands under the supervision of the Department of the Interior.

1920—Federal Water Power Act placed development of water power on navigable rivers in the hands of the Federal Power Commission.

1920—A Federal leasing act for coal, oil, and gas lands was passed; it superseded the old mining-claim procedure.

1920—Petroleum industry began to use the cracking process of making gasoline from crude oil, practically doubling the yield of gasoline.

1921—Initial application of insecticides by airplane was performed by the Ohio Experiment Station in conjunction with the United States Air Service.

1921—The National Conference on State Parks was organized to stimulate the movement for the provision of outdoor recreational opportunities.

1922—Isaak Walton League was founded.

1923—The Monticello Foundation was established to care for the Thomas Jefferson house.

1924—Congress authorized co-operation between the government and private owners in fire protection and forest planting.

1924—Federal Oil Conservation Board was created by the Federal government to study oil conservation.

1924—The Ohio River Interstate Stream Conservation Agreement was made for the purpose of conserving interstate streams.

1925—Clark-McNary Act authorized Federal-state co-operation in production of planting stock for forestry.

1926—The American Shore and Beach Preservation Association was formed.

1926—Voluntary curtailment of oil production in Seminole area, Oklahoma, marked the beginning of "proration period."

1927—The leasing principle was extended to sulphur lands.

1928—Congress authorized the establishment of a national system of regional forest experiment stations.

1928—Mississippi Flood Control Act authorized extension and strengthening of the levee system.

1928—The Department of Justice rendered the opinion that, of the Northern Pacific Railroad land grant, title to more than 3,000,000 acres should be forfeited.

1929—2,800,000 acres of Northern Pacific Railroad land grant was forfeited to the Federal government.

1929—The Rio Grande Compact was made by Texas, Colorado, and New Mexico to provide for the use of the waters of the river by these states.

1930—The Committee on the Public Domain was appointed by President Hoover to study public land problems.

1931—The Federal government established a number of experiment stations to determine the losses of soil and water that occur under a wide variety of conditions.

1931—Oil States Advisory Committee, composed of representatives of ten oil-producing states, was formed to formulate plans for stabilizing the oil industry through interstate action.

1933—Tennessee Valley Authority was created.

1933—Civilian Conservation Corps was established to engage in extensive Park, reforestation and other conservation work.

APPENDIX

1933—Consolidation of all Federal park and monument areas under the National Park Service of the Department of the Interior.

1933—The Soil Erosion Service was established under the National Industrial Recovery Act.

1933—The establishment of a great shelter belt extending from Canada south through the prairie states was undertaken.

1933—The Agricultural Adjustment Administration encouraged shifting of acreages to crops which would conserve the land.

1934—Taylor Grazing Act placed 80,000,000 acres of the public domain under the Department of the Interior to administer, to stop injury to the public lands by preventing overgrazing.

1934—The most serious dust storms on record in the history of the country occurred.

1934—National Resources Board was created and made the first national survey of land-use conditions in the United States. (In 1936 changed to National Resources Committee; since 1939 National Resources Planning Board).

1934-1935—All unappropriated public lands open to settlement were withdrawn from entry by executive order.

1935—Historic Sites Act provided for a survey of historic sites and preservation of sites of national importance.

1935—Connally "Hot Oil" act designed to aid conservation of petroleum was passed.

1935—The Soil Conservation Service was established in the Department of Agriculture to propagate the use of soil conservation practices in agriculture.

1935—The Resettlement Administration was created by executive order to conserve human and natural resources.

1936—Soil Conservation and Domestic Allotment Act established grants-in-aid for soil conservation.

1937—A Federal Act was passed to promote conservation of helium gas.

1938—Mount Olympus National Park was created.

1938—O. & C. Revested Land Administration was established with offices in Portland, Oregon.

1939—First appropriation ($37,500) was made for fire protection on the public domain in Alaska.

1939—Bureau of Fisheries, formerly in the Department of Commerce, and the Bureau of Biological Survey of the Department of Agriculture, were transferred to the Department of the Interior. These two services were combined under the Fish and Wildlife Service of the Department of the Interior.

1940—Soil Conservation Service functions relating to Interior Department lands were transferred from the Agriculture to the Department of the Interior.

1940—Office of the Assistant to the Secretary in charge of Land Utilization was established in the Department of the Interior to direct soil and moisture conservation activities and to administer the forests on

AMERICA'S NATURAL WEALTH

285,000,000 acres of land under the jurisdiction of the Department of the Interior.

1940—Kings Canyon National Park was created.

1942—Civilian Conservation Corps was liquidated.

INDEX

241

INDEX

INDEX

243

INDEX

Office of Education, 215
Ohio Company of Associates, 128
Ohio River, 67, 68, 82, 83
  flood, 82, 83
Oil, 27, 43, 44, 53, 54
Olympic Mountain region, 178
Olympic National Park, 117
O'Neill, John J., 40
Organic matter, loss of, 137

Paper, consumption and production
  of, 97
Park, Parkway and Recreational
  Study Act, 220
Parks, 163-207, 219, 220
  cabins in, 204
  campers in, 203, 204
  concessions in, 182-207
  expansion of, 188
  government of, 171-207
  in England, 164
  in Indiana, 186-190, 201, 202, 204
  inns in, 197, 198, 199, 203
  maintenance of, 170-207
  national, 165ff.
  preservation of, 195-207
  regulations for, 201, 202
  service areas in, 196, 201, 206, 207
  state, 167-207
  supporting the, 182-207
  visitors to, 177-207
Paul, J. W., 42
Penn, William, Fundamental Ordinance, 212
Petroleum, 54, 55
Phosphorus, 139-142
Pinchot, Gifford, 112
Plastics, 98, 99
Plymouth Colony, 212
Population, 149, 150, 151
Potash, 58, 95
Potassium, 139, 140
Potomac River, 72
Powell, Major J. W., 84, 85, 134, 137
Power, 23, 31-37, 41
Preservation of park property, 195-
  207
President's committee to investigate

governmental reorganization, 12,
  13, 16, 17, 18
Provincial American, The, 156
Public Domain, The, 128
Public domain, 128, 134
Public Works Administration, 225

Reclamation Act of *1902,* 85
Reclamation, Bureau of, 222
Recreational centers, 190
"Recreational Use of Land in the
  United States," 171-176
Regulations, park, 201, 202, 205, 206
Reorganization, governmental, 12-22,
  87, 88
Reservoirs, 192
Review of Reviews, 3-8
Rice, George S., 42
Riparian rights, 77
Rise of American Civilization, The,
  129
Roosevelt, Franklin Delano, 8, 10,
  15, 16, 18, 117, 214-218, 225
Roosevelt, Theodore, 112, 118, 212,
  213
  Conservation Commission, 118
Run-off, the, 64-71

Safety measures in mining, 52
Salt, 193
Schwartz, H. H., 131
Schurz, Carl, 111
Scrap metal, 45, 46
Scripps-Howard press, 21, 22
Sears, Dr. Paul B., 146, 147
Secretary of the Interior, 84, 85, 220
Senate Document No. *676,* 213
Service areas in parks, 196-201, 206,
  207
Sewage, 67-71, 141, 142
Share cropping, 142
Smith, Assistant Forester Herbert
  A., 117
Soil Conservation Service, 221, 222
Soil, *see* Land
Spanish law, 77
Sphere, The, 20
State parks, 167-207, 219, 220
States, land grants to, 132, 133

INDEX